The Plant in Relation
to Water

The Plant in Relation to Water

by

R. O. Knight, B.Sc.

Assistant Biology Master,
Chislehurst and Sidcup Grammar School for Boys

Heinemann Educational Books Ltd
London

Heinemann Educational Books Ltd
LONDON MELBOURNE TORONTO
CAPE TOWN SINGAPORE
AUCKLAND HONG KONG
IBADAN

Published by
Heinemann Educational Books Ltd
48 Charles Street, London W.1

Printed in Great Britain by
Bookprint Limited, Kingswood, Surrey

Preface

This book is an attempt to present a comprehensive and up-to-date treatment of a major topic in plant science. It is intended to serve the needs of pupils in school Sixth Forms, as well as their teachers, but a large proportion of the material presented here will be found valuable also for students of Botany in Universities. To assist the more advanced reader, numerous references are made to important original papers and review articles.

Water is the most abundant naturally occurring chemical compound. It plays a vital role in the maintenance of life, a fact which receives emphasis when it is realized that usually between eight- and nine-tenths of the weight of a living cell is due to the water it contains. Not only is water an essential constituent of protoplasm, it is also the only medium in which the multiplicity of metabolic reactions can proceed, and in which the transport of important substances can take place. These last features are due to the enormous effectiveness of water as a solvent. In addition, water fulfils a vital role in the support of plant tissues, besides being an essential raw material for the all-important process of photosynthesis. It is not surprising that the availability of moisture is a major factor governing the distribution of plants over the Earth's surface.

The treatment of the subject matter here may be considered under three headings – **physiological**, **structural** and **ecological**, although none of these aspects can be viewed in isolation. The physiological aspects present perhaps the greatest difficulties, since many problems, such as the question of active water uptake, remain unsolved. As in any branch of physiology, each new discovery often opens up fresh avenues of inquiry and raises further questions, so that our understanding can seemingly never be complete.

No apology is made for the inclusion of some material on plant structure. All too often, structure is studied in isolation, and even then given scanty treatment, especially nowadays. Here, a careful attempt has been made to relate structure and function, both at the cellular and higher levels of differentiation. By this means, it is felt, the study of both is made more comprehensible and more interesting.

The chapters follow what seems to the author to be a logical sequence, and the fact that the section on ecology is presented last in no way implies that it is considered to be the least important, or the least interesting aspect of the subject matter. Indeed, with the ever-increasing magnitude of the world food problem, some of the most valuable work in applied science today is concerned with the problems of irrigation, and the efficient utilization of often very limited water supplies in crop production.

In order to increase the usefulness of the book, directions for carrying out simple practical work are included in the text, and there is a list of works for further reading.

In this book the following units of length are used:

$$\mu = 1 \text{ micron} \qquad\qquad = 10^{-3} \text{ mm}$$
$$m\mu = 1 \text{ millimicron} \qquad = 10^{-6} \text{ mm}$$
$$\text{Å} = 1 \text{ Ångström unit} \qquad = 10^{-7} \text{ mm}$$

Contents

Preface   v

List of Plates   viii

Acknowledgements   ix

1. Some Characteristics of Water and Aqueous Systems   1

2. The Parenchymatous Cell   15

3. Water Relationships of Cells and Tissues   24

4. The Path of Water   41

5. Transpiration   61

6. The Absorption and Ascent of Water   90

7. Water in the Environment   105

Bibliography   142

List of Practical Directions   143

Index   144

List of Plates

facing page

PLATE I. Electron micrograph of small parts of two meristematic cortical cells   20

PLATE II. (1) Plasmolysed cells
(b) 'Leaf skeleton' of a dicotyledon   21

PLATE III. Open stoma of *Rumex acetosa*   52

PLATE IV. (1) Open stoma of *Fuchsia*
(b) and (c) Open and closed stomata of *Trades-
cantia paludosa*   53

Acknowledgements

I wish to express my gratitude to Dr K. E. Cockshull of the University of Reading, G. A. Strafford, B.Sc., M. Inst. Biol., of King William College, I.O.M., and W. F. Wheeler, M.A., of the Royal Grammar School, Worcester, all of whom read the manuscript at various stages, and from whom detailed and constructive criticisms were forthcoming. As a result of their suggestions, many additions and other improvements were made to the original draft. For any inaccuracies remaining, the author holds himself entirely responsible.

Thanks are also due to Dr B. E. Juniper, of the Botany School, Oxford, and to Professor O. V. S. Heath of the University of Reading, who supplied the photographs reproduced in Plates I and IV respectively. I also wish to thank Professor F. J. Veihmeyer, of the Department of Irrigation, University of California, for his ideas on soil moisture, and the authorities of King's College, London, for affording me the necessary library facilities.

For permission to use material (Fig. 25) from their published works, I am grateful to the McGraw-Hill Book Co., Inc. and to the Controller of Her Majesty's Stationery Office (Maps I, II and III).

Finally, I should like to thank my wife, not only for assisting with the preparation of the index and of certain drawings, but also for her patience throughout the protracted period of preparation of this book.

R. O. Knight
January 1965

CHAPTER ONE

Some Characteristics of Water and Aqueous Systems

In this chapter, selected properties of aqueous systems are discussed. In view of its relevance to the content of subsequent chapters, the reader should familiarize himself with this material before proceeding further.

1. Cohesion

Cohesion is the tendency of the molecules of an element or compound to be held together by forces of mutual attraction which exist between them. It is one example of the attractive forces experienced between any two particles of matter, the magnitude of such forces depending upon the masses of the particles and their distance apart.

In the case of gases, the cohesive forces between molecules are low, largely because of their low molecular weight. This means that the molecules offer little resistance to changes in their separation distances, and so the volume of a given mass of gas can easily be altered by changes in the external pressure. In the case of liquids, the cohesive forces are much greater, so that the extent to which they can be stretched or compressed is very small.

When water, the hydride of oxygen, is compared with the hydrides of the other elements in Group VIb in the Periodic Table, its physical properties are found to deviate markedly from those which might be expected of it. These properties should show a steady gradation from one member to the next in the series but Fig. 1 makes it clear that its melting and boiling points, for example, are extraordinarily high. In fact we would expect, from their low molecular weights, that all these compounds would be gaseous at ordinary temperatures. This unexpected behaviour of water can be interpreted in terms of a special property known as hydrogen bonding, which has the effect of increasing the cohesive forces between the molecules. Within each molecule, the positive electrostatic charge on each hydrogen atom is only partially neutralized by the negatively charged oxygen atom. The residual positive charge on the hydrogen serves to attract the oxygen of another, nearby water molecule, so that each molecule behaves, in effect, like a minute bar magnet. Each is bonded to, and closely associated with, four other molecules, so that the overall effect is one of an array of tetrahedra, one molecule being at the centre, and

1

one at each of the four corners. As a result of this molecular association, much more heat is required to separate the molecules from one another and to raise their kinetic energy to the level at which they will vaporize. This means that water does not evaporate so readily as

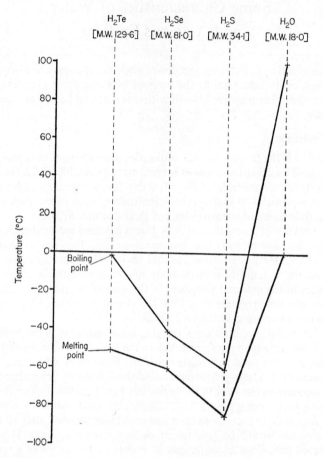

FIG. 1. Melting points and boiling points of Group VI b hydrides.

would otherwise be the case and that the boiling point is greatly elevated. It should also be noted that the specific heat of water is also abnormally high, so that more heat is needed to raise the temperature of a given mass of water through, say, 1 deg. C than is the case with most other ordinary liquids. This undoubtedly helps to minimize the effect on living organisms of any sharp temperature changes which might occur in their surroundings. Finally, the increased intermolecular forces raise the viscosity of water, and hence increase its resistance to flow through, for example, narrow xylem elements.

Hydrogen bonds are only formed between hydrogen and the electronegative elements oxygen, fluorine, chlorine and nitrogen. Methane, for example, whose molecular weight is close to that of water, forms no hydrogen bonds, and its boiling point is only $-161°$ C.

Upon the cohesive properties of water molecules depend such processes as the ascent of water in tall trees, and also the dehiscence of some types of sporangia in the lower plant groups, as well as the stamens of Angiosperms. Hydrogen bonding also plays an important part in relation to cellulose (p. 18) and to protoplasmic proteins (p. 21).

2. Adhesion

Adhesion, as distinct from cohesion, is the tendency of molecules to be attracted to those of a different type. Again, intermolecular forces are involved. If a flat glass sheet is placed in contact with a water surface, and then slowly raised from it, a short column of liquid can be drawn from the surface, thus demonstrating adhesion between water and glass. Similar adhesive forces exist between the walls of xylem elements and their fluid contents. These forces are believed to be very considerable, perhaps of the order of 1,000 atmospheres. Many liquids, including the xylem contents, contain more than one type of molecule, and here forces of cohesion between like, and forces of adhesion between unlike particles are involved.

3. Capillarity

It is well known that if an open glass tube is held vertically with one end just below a water surface, the liquid will rise in the tube to a height above the surface which varies inversely with the diameter of the bore. Thus whilst a tube of 1 mm diameter will support a water column only about 30 mm high, the corresponding height for, say, one of the narrower xylem elements of diameter 0.02 mm will be about 1,500 mm. The absorbent properties of such materials as lamp-wicks, blotting paper and newspaper are due to capillarity, the very fine spaces between the fibres acting as the capillaries. Also, cell walls often contain very large numbers of minute water-filled capillaries between the structural units of the actual wall material (see p. 18). Capillarity plays an important part in maintaining the water content of these spaces.

Capillarity is explained on the basis of intermolecular forces between the various components of the system, but the details of this are too complex for discussion here.

4. The Colloidal State

Provided that no chemical reaction takes place, a powdered solid mixed with a liquid may behave in one of three main ways. (a) Depending upon its density, it may float at the surface, or else form a suspension which eventually settles under the influence of gravity. In neither case is it visibly affected by the liquid. (b) It may dissolve to form a solution. In the case of electrolytes the molecules dissociate into ions which become evenly distributed by diffusion. Non-electrolytes undergo no dissociation, but the individual molecules similarly become dispersed. The largest particles present in a true solution are thus molecules or ions. It should be noted here that water is undoubtedly the most effective known solvent. Since all organic reactions in living organisms will only proceed when the reactants are in the dissolved state, and since most materials are transported in solution, the usefulness of water as a biological liquid is again apparent. (c) It may form a **colloidal system** with the liquid. Here, the solid (called the **disperse phase**) is distributed throughout the liquid (referred to as the **dispersion medium**) in a very finely-divided state. The size of the particles is intermediate between those of true solutions, which are invisible, and those of suspensions, which can be seen, at least under the microscope.

If a powerful beam of light is directed through a colloidal system and viewed at right angles through a microscope, each particle scatters a little light, and appears as a bright dot. This scattering of light is called the Tyndall effect. Each spot of light is in a state of continuous and violent agitation. The motion of the particles is due to bombardment by the rapidly moving molecules of the dispersion medium and is called the Brownian movement, because a similar effect was noted by Brown in 1827, not in a colloid, but in a suspension of minute particles obtained from disrupted pollen grains. It should be clearly understood that in colloidal systems, the particles themselves are too small to be seen; it is the optical effects which they produce which are visible in this way. In true solutions no Brownian movement is visible, since the particles are too small even to scatter light.

A solid dispersed in a liquid is by no means the only type of colloidal system which exists. Both disperse phase and dispersion medium may be gaseous, liquid, or solid. Some examples are given in Table 1. For present purposes, only colloids where water is the dispersion medium need be considered.

The most important feature of colloids is the vast surface area of contact which exists between the two phases. This results from the fact that the more finely-divided a given amount of matter becomes, the greater is its surface area. The size of colloidal particles lies approximately within the range 1 mμ to 100 mμ. A solid cube of side

Dispersion Medium	Disperse Phase	Example
Liquid (mainly water)	*Liquid* (minute fatty droplets)	Homogenized milk
Liquid (water)	*Solid* (pectin molecules)	Table jelly
Gas (air)	*Solid* (minute soot particles)	Tobacco smoke
Gas (air)	*Liquid* (minute aqueous droplets)	Mists

TABLE 1. Some types of colloidal systems

1 cm has a total surface area of only 6 sq. cm, but if this were broken into particles of colloidal dimensions, the surface area would be of the order of 1,000,000 sq. cm. Such surfaces provide sites upon which chemical compounds can be held in the form of adsorbed films whilst, for example, reactions take place between them. This is of great importance in the case of protoplasm. Enzymes, for example, are protein molecules of colloidal dimensions, and they are believed to form a transitory intermediate association with their substrate by adsorption which enables the reaction which they catalyse to be brought about.

There are several distinct physical classes of colloids. Three of these, the **sol**, the **emulsion** and the **gel** are important, since protoplasm can at certain times possess properties characteristic of each of these types. Both sols and emulsions have a high degree of fluidity, but whereas a sol consists of a solid dispersed in a liquid, an emulsion exists where both components are liquid. Gels contain both solid and liquid phases, but are much more rigid than sols, and show no Brownian movement. At the same time they are somewhat elastic. Agar and gelatin are familiar examples of gels. Under suitable conditions, gels can rapidly form sols (a process called solation) and sols can change into gels (gelation). The setting of a table jelly is an example of gelation. Here, as little as one part of gelatin is sufficient to gelate 100 parts of water, provided that the temperature and pH are correct. Protoplasm readily undergoes sol $\rightleftharpoons$ gel transformations. Some colloids (e.g. some paints) are thixotropic. This means that they are gels when at rest, but solate rapidly on being mechanically disturbed.

Gelatin and protoplasm are examples of an important group of colloids called **hydrophilic** colloids. These have the following properties: (a) There is great affinity between the disperse phase and the water. Water surrounds the particles in the form of adsorbed films, and it is this hydration of the particles which keeps them dispersed, and prevents them from aggregating into larger particles which would settle out. In order to bring about precipitation, the particles must be dehydrated by the addition of such a substance as alcohol. (b) They are much more viscous, and have a lower surface tension, than water. (c) They are not precipitated by the addition of small amounts of electrolytes.

In contrast to such colloids, certain substances, notably the 'noble' metals, gold, platinum and silver, form **hydrophobic** colloids. These have the following properties: (a) There is no affinity between the two phases, and drastic methods may have to be used to bring them into the colloidal state. (b) Their surface tension and viscosity differ little from those of water. (c) There are no adsorbed water films and the particles are maintained in the dispersed state entirely by the like (either positive or negative) charges which they carry. Colloidal particles of gold, for example, are always negatively charged. Small amounts of added electrolyte are sufficient to neutralize some of these charges, so that the particles then coagulate into units large enough to settle under the influence of gravity.

An important feature of hydrophilic colloids is that they are often capable of absorbing great quantities of water, a process called **imbibition**, which is accompanied by notable swelling. This is especially true of protoplasm in the gel state. Absolutely dry colloids absorb the first traces of water with a tremendous force, which may, in the case of dry seeds for example, exceed 1,000 atmospheres. In some cases considerable heat may be generated, as when perfectly dry starch is moistened. Since these first traces of water are so firmly held, they are difficult to remove, even at high temperatures, because the vapour pressure of the water is artificially lowered by the imbibitional forces. For this reason also, the freezing point of the water is usually well below 0° C. As the amount of imbibed water in a colloid increases, the imbibitional and swelling forces decrease. This less firmly held water is much more easily removed by high temperature treatment, for example, or by the application of pressure.

Imbibition is of great importance in relation to protoplasm (p. 20), cell wall materials (p. 18), and certain soil particles (p. 111).

5. Diffusion

In order to carry out its many activities, a living cell must obtain essential raw materials. Also, toxic products of metabolism must be removed. For many such transportation processes, both between and within cells, diffusion is responsible.

Diffusion may be defined as **the net movement of a substance from a region where it is more highly concentrated to a region of lower concentration, due to the inherent motion of its constituent particles**. Perhaps the simplest way of demonstrating diffusion visually is to drop a crystal of a readily soluble chemical which gives a strongly coloured solution, into a large amount of water in a beaker. Potassium permanganate or methylene blue are suitable compounds. The beaker must be undisturbed, and maintained at constant temperature so that water currents do not affect the distribution of the solute. Very soon, a shell of darkly coloured solution forms around the crystal, which gradually shades off into the colourless bulk of the liquid. Gradually, after the crystal has completely dissolved, the colour becomes uniform throughout. This takes many hours, but when complete it indicates that the dissolved particles have spread uniformly through the solution. The cause of this movement is that the molecules or ions of a solute are in a state of continuous and violent motion. The movement is entirely at random, each particle proceeding at high speed in a straight line until hitting another particle, when both are deflected, in the manner of two colliding billiard balls. In the vicinity of the dissolving crystal there are, initially, far more randomly moving solute particles than in the surrounding medium. Clearly, therefore, more of these will move out of this concentrated zone per second than will travel in the opposite direction, and the visible effect of this is the gradual evening-up of the coloration. Eventually, when the coloration reaches uniformity, the same number of particles enter any given zone of the solution per second as leave it. At this stage, when there is no **net** movement of particles from any region to another, diffusion is said to have ceased.

It will be clear from the above that, for diffusion to take place, a concentration difference must exist inside the system. In the case of the dissolving permanganate crystal referred to, there is no abrupt change in concentration to give a sharp boundary between deep magenta and colourless regions, but instead there is a gradual shading-off of the coloration. A **concentration gradient** is said to exist across the system.

Whenever diffusion is taking place, it is not difficult to conceive the process as being the result of a type of pressure difference. This point becomes clearer if another specific case is considered. Suppose that a strong brine solution is placed in a Cellophane or parchment tube which is then lowered into a beaker containing a weaker solution, or water. The levels of the two solutions should be the same. Although the cellophane or parchment prevents mixing of the two liquids by convection currents, it contains pores large enough to permit the passage of both water and solute particles. Since there are more Na^+ and Cl^- ions inside the tube than outside, more will strike the membrane and pass through the pores per second in an outward direction than in the reverse direction. Thus, in terms of the solute particles only, there is a net pressure difference between the two sides of the membrane, resulting from the difference in the number of impacts per second, which in turn, results from the difference in concentrations of the two solutions. Thus the **diffusion pressure** of the salt particles is greater inside the tube than outside. Ultimately, of course, the concentrations of solution on each side of the membrane become equalized. There is a net movement of salt particles outwards, and a corresponding net movement of water molecules inwards, so that the levels of liquid remain the same in each part of the apparatus.

Diffusion is not a property confined to dissolved substances. It is shown also by gases and liquids. Rates of diffusion of gases are much faster than those of substances dissolved in liquids. This is because the molecules of liquids are larger, heavier and more closely packed than those of gases, so slowing down the movement of any particles distributed in them to a much greater extent. Convection currents and other 'mass flow' disturbances frequently obscure the true diffusion process, but even in still air it is very easy to detect a slight leakage of coal-gas, for example. If a gas is introduced into a previously evacuated chamber, the diffusion process is, as would be expected, very fast indeed. Another important factor governing diffusion rates is the mass of the particles, lighter ones travelling faster. The size of particle is important too. A large molecule will diffuse more slowly under given conditions than a smaller one of equal mass. Colloidal particles, which are large and heavy by molecular standards, are characterized by diffusion rates which are very slow or nil.

In the case of a liquid in contact with a gas, molecules of the liquid, by dint of their inherent kinetic energy, continuously escape from the surface into the gaseous phase in the form of vapour. If the system is in a closed vessel, the gas soon becomes saturated with the rapidly moving molecules of the vapour, which bombard the walls of the vessel, and exert a pressure on them. This pressure is known as the **saturation vapour pressure** of the liquid, and its value is constant for a given liquid at a given temperature. At higher temperatures the air or other gas can hold more vapour, and the saturation vapour pressure increases. At 20° C, for example, the value for water is 17.5 mm of mercury, whilst at 25° C the figure is 23.9 mm. If the air is not fully saturated, the actual vapour pressure will naturally be less than the value at saturation. Clearly, vapour pressure is due to the same force which actuates diffusion, i.e. the inherent motion of the particles. If a substance is dissolved in a liquid, the motion of the particles of the liquid is restricted, and the vapour pressure accordingly lowered. The amount of the lowering of the vapour pressure depends upon the amount of solute present.

In biological systems, diffusion operates advantageously. As an example, we may consider the way in which oxygen is obtained by the cytoplasm of the cells of a root. There is some dissolved oxygen present in the cytoplasm, but as this becomes depleted in a particular region by respiratory processes, its concentration falls. Consequently, more dissolved oxygen automatically diffuses along the concentration gradient set up, from regions of the cell where it is more highly concentrated. The general lowering of the oxygen concentration in the cell causes more to diffuse from adjoining cells, and the whole process is continuous in this way right through to the root surface, where the oxygen from the soil air spaces is dissolving in the water films covering the root surface. Carbon dioxide will diffuse outwards, since here the concentration gradient is in the reverse direction, due to the continued production of the dissolved gas in the cytoplasm as a respiratory waste product. This illustrates the point that diffusion can take place in more than one direction across a system when more than one substance is involved. It is the direction of the concentration gradient of each separate substance that governs its own direction of diffusion. Since diffusion in liquids is a slow process, it is important that an adequate system of air spaces is present in plants, so that no living cell is too far from supplies of oxygen. Thus the air space system in soil must be maintained to allow respiration of roots. This is one reason why waterlogged soils are so unfavourable to plant growth.

Diffusion across membranes is not usually so straightforward a process as in the cases so far considered, however. This is because membranes are not equally permeable to all types of molecules. In the case of such synthetic membranes as parchment or Cellophane, this **differential permeability** is probably chiefly due to the membrane acting as a microsieve, excluding large particles and allowing passage of smaller ones, such as water molecules or ions of salts, depending on the pore size. This makes it possible to separate a mixture of a colloid and a freely diffusible substance, a principle which is useful commercially, in a well-known technique called **dialysis**. For example, during the course of their preparation, certain proteinaceous antitoxic serums are precipitated by the addition of ammonium sulphate, which then has to be removed. The precipitate is dialysed in sacs of Cellophane, whose pore size is such that it is completely permeable to the ions of ammonium sulphate solution, but impermeable to the serum. The sac is washed continuously with running tap water for at least twenty-four hours. The ammonium sulphate diffuses out into the water, whilst the product remains inside, because the protein molecules of the serum, besides being non-diffusible, are too large to pass through the pores in the Cellophane. Even the last traces of ammonium sulphate can be removed in this way.

6. Osmosis

We are now in a position to consider the case where two solutions with the same components but of different concentrations are separated, not by a completely permeable partition, but by one permeable only to the solvent. Such a system may be obtained using the simple assembly depicted in Fig. 2, which can be easily improvised or obtained commercially. It consists essentially of two curved glass limbs which fit together to form a U-shaped apparatus. The lower parts of the limbs are expanded so as to form two wide chambers. The chambers may be joined by means of a short, stout, rubber tube, so that a tight, leak-proof joint may be made. The rubber tube is pushed partway into one of the chambers, and the differentially permeable membrane is carefully stretched across the other end of the rubber tube. The other chamber is then pushed over the tube and membrane.

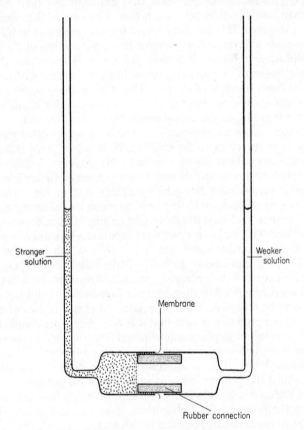

FIG. 2. A simple osmometer.

Strong sugar solution is carefully introduced into, say, the left-hand tube so as to partly fill it, and either a weaker sugar solution, or distilled water, is added to the same height in the right-hand limb. A gradual but appreciable rise in the level of the fluid in the left-hand tube takes place, paralleled by a corresponding fall in the opposite side of the apparatus. If success is to be achieved, the join between the membrane and the two tubes must be firm, and the membrane uncreased, so that no fluid can escape. (It will be realized that if a comparable system were to be set up using different solute and/or solvent, a different type of membrane might be necessary. Whether a membrane is suitable for a particular system will depend largely on the sizes of pores and particles involved, and sometimes also on such factors as whether there is any chemical interaction between the membrane and any part of the system.) Either of the following membranes gives good results: (1) A portion of dried pig's bladder (obtainable commercially), de-fatted by soaking in ether. (2) A piece cut from Cellophane dialysis tubing which has been soaked overnight in water (this is again obtainable commercially, in varying degrees of porosity). The membrane obtained from an egg by dissolving away the shell in vinegar may be successful, but it is easily punctured during fitting.

In order to explain the movement of liquid which takes place in this and similar situations, we must consider the diffusion pressures of both solute and solvent. The diffusion pressure of the solute is clearly greater in the more concentrated solution than the dilute one. That of the solvent, however, is greater in the dilute solution since, as was noted in the last section (p. 8), the presence of solute particles lowers the activity, and hence the diffusion pressure, of the solvent molecules. Because of this effect, all solutions are said to show a **diffusion pressure deficit** with respect to the pure solvent. The more concentrated the solution, the more the activity of the solvent molecules is lowered, and the higher is the diffusion pressure deficit. The greater the diffusion pressure deficit of a solution, the less is the diffusion pressure of the solvent molecules which it contains.

As a result of the difference in diffusion pressures, solvent molecules diffuse into the more concentrated solution from the weaker one. Diffusion of solute in the opposite direction across the membrane is prevented by the fact that the membrane is impermeable to these particles, and so only one-way traffic actually takes place. Such a movement of solvent only, which is clearly a special case of diffusion, is called **osmosis**. It differs from the example on p. 7 in that a differentially permeable membrane is necessary, so that only solvent, and not solute, passes across.

The above situation is, however, a somewhat ideal one and, in fact, most membranes are to some extent 'leaky', i.e. they are not absolutely impermeable to the solute particles. If the membrane is only slightly 'leaky', the effect on osmosis over a short time-period is negligible, since few solute particles penetrate. If the effect is very marked, the situation approaches that described on p. 7 and the osmotic effect is small and temporary.

Osmosis may be defined as **the net passage of a solvent from a** solution (or from a region of pure solvent) into another solution of greater diffusion pressure deficit, across a membrane more permeable to solvent than to solute. Under ordinary circumstances, the flow takes place from a weaker solution towards a more concentrated one, since, as was stated above, the more concentrated solution shows the greater diffusion pressure deficit.

The most important solvent in living organisms is, of course, water. Since each living cell behaves as a separate unit enclosed in a differentially permeable membrane, it is easy to see the relevance of osmosis to the movement of water within tissues. There is no simple or single explanation of the cause of differential permeability in cell membranes. As was mentioned earlier in connection with diffusion, some synthetic membranes act as microsieves, and it is probable that this plays some part in the case of natural membranes. However, it is certainly not the whole explanation, and the chemical nature of both the membrane and the substances with which it is in contact is undoubtedly of great importance. Also, the permeability characteristics of cell membranes are greatly affected by alterations in any factor which in any way affects the living protoplasm. (See p. 25.)

In experiments such as that described above, the rise of the liquid column does not proceed indefinitely, and the circumstances under which it comes to a halt will now be considered. Initially, the only force involved is the difference between the diffusion pressure deficits of the two solutions. A second factor soon becomes important, however. This is the downward pressure exerted on the left-hand side of the membrane due to the difference in height of the two columns, which is numerically equal to the product of the excess height of the left-hand column and the density of the liquid composing it. The important point to appreciate is that when this pressure becomes equal to the difference in diffusion pressure deficits of the two solutions, osmosis will cease, and the level remain constant.

It will be clear that the main factor governing the height to which the column will rise, is the initial difference in concentrations (i.e. diffusion pressure deficits) between the two solutions. For a given solution inside the left-hand tube, this will obviously be greatest when pure water is in the opposite arm. Also, the more concentrated the solution, the greater is its osmotic capacity. It is useful to be able to measure this capacity, and to do this, the term **osmotic pressure** is generally employed. The osmotic pressure of a solution is **the pressure which must be applied to that solution when separated from pure solvent by a membrane permeable only to the solvent, in order to exactly counterbalance the diffusion pressure deficit of the solution, and so prevent osmosis.** Applying this to the U-tube experiment, the osmotic pressure of the solution in the left-hand tube at equilibrium is equal to the difference in height of the two columns, multiplied by the density of the solution, provided that the other limb is occupied by pure water. This value is not the same as the osmotic pressure of the original solution, because this has been diluted by the incoming water.

The osmotic pressure of a solution is usually expressed in terms of atmospheric pressure. From the discussion on the previous two pages, and from the above definition, it should be clear to the reader that, under normal circumstances, the osmotic pressure of a given solution is numerically equal to its diffusion pressure deficit. This is an important point to realize.

Although the term 'osmotic pressure' receives wide usage in relation to solutions, the reader will realize that only under certain special conditions is there any real pressure effect, i.e., the solution must be separated from another, of different concentration by a differentially permeable membrane. Even then, the most ideal conditions are rarely, if ever, met with in nature, where so many complex factors are involved, and the full osmotic pressure of which a solution is potentially capable of bringing about is seldom manifested. Certainly in the case of a solution in a bottle on a laboratory shelf, it is misleading to speak of its having an osmotic pressure. In the remainder of this book, therefore, the term 'osmotic pressure' will be replaced by **osmotic potential** wherever, as is usually the case, this seems more appropriate.

There are certain objections to employing a method such as that described above for the accurate determination of the osmotic potential of a solution. The most important is that, as already mentioned, the solution suffers great dilution. Secondly, the membranes are never, in practice, completely impermeable to solute molecules. As they diffuse across the 'leaky' membrane, the concentration difference lessens, and the column gradually falls. Such methods are therefore only really satisfactory for demonstration purposes. These difficulties can be avoided by using a type of apparatus introduced by the German botanist Pfeffer, who in 1877 determined the osmotic potentials of various strengths of sugar solutions. Into carefully prepared unglazed clay cylinders he poured a dilute solution of cupric sulphate. The cylinders were then placed in a bath containing dilute potassium ferrocyanide solution. The two solutions diffused towards one another, and where they met, a precipitate of cupric ferrocyanide was deposited in the pores of the clay. Such chemical membranes give good results, if prepared with meticulous care and cleanliness. The solution under investigation is poured into the pot, whose open end is then secured to a mercury manometer. The pot is then placed in pure water. Owing to the high density of mercury, a considerable pressure can be measured without much change in the volume of the contents of the pot, so that little dilution takes place. A similar type of apparatus (Fig. 3) has been used for accurate determination by Berkeley and

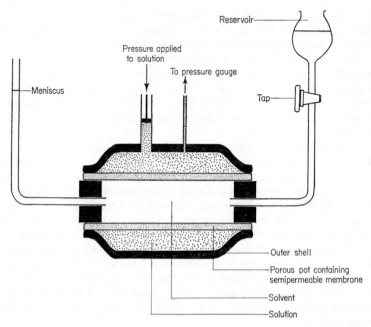

FIG. 3. Diagram of the type of apparatus used by Berkeley and
Hartley in the determination of osmotic potentials.

Hartley. Here, the externally applied pressure necessary to **prevent**
osmosis was measured, so avoiding any dilution.

Such accurate determinations indicate that for dilute sucrose
solutions the Gas Laws are approximately obeyed, i.e., $PV = nRT$,
where P is the osmotic potential of the solution, V the number of litres
of solution, n the number of gram-molecules of solute, R the gas
constant 0.083 litre-atmospheres, and T the absolute temperature.
Thus, at constant temperature, the osmotic potential of a dilute
sucrose solution is approximately proportional to its concentration.
At 20° C, for example, a 0.10 molar solution has an osmotic potential
of 2.6 atmospheres, the corresponding values for 0.20 and 0.40 molar
solutions being 5.3 and 11.1 atmospheres respectively. This principle
is valid for most non-electrolytes. Electrolytes, however, dissociate
into ions when dissolved in water, to a degree dependent upon the
dilution. Therefore, since the osmotic potentials of solutions depend
upon the number of particles present, those of electrolytes are greater
than those of non-electrolytes at a given concentration.

Two solutions of any substances which have the same osmotic
potential are said to be **isotonic**. If a solution A has a higher osmotic
potential than a solution B, A is said to be **hypertonic** to B, and B
hypotonic to A.

CHAPTER TWO

The Parenchymatous Cell

Parenchyma is a type of tissue composed of thin-walled cells with living protoplasts. It accounts for the major part of the structure of herbaceous stems and roots, as well as of leaves. It is also an essential component of woody stems and roots, though here it occurs less extensively. Some types of thin-walled living cells, such as cambium, and phloem sieve elements, are normally excluded from the meaning of the term parenchyma, due to their greater specialization. Some of the different forms which parenchyma can take are described in Chapter Four. Here, we are concerned not with the tissue as a whole, but rather with the structure of the individual cell. Since nearly all the living plant tissues are parenchymatous, the water relationships of these cells, which cannot be fully understood without some detailed knowledge of their structure, are of great importance.

1. Gross Features

Although parenchymatous cells vary considerably in size and form, all share certain fundamental characteristics. The principal structural features common to most such cells are included in Fig. 4 (which indicates the structures visible in the unstained, living state, under the high power of the light microscope) and Plate I (which shows certain features in great detail as rendered visible by the electron microscope). Fig. 4 plainly shows that the greatest part is occupied by a fluid-filled **vacuole**. The vacuolar fluid consists of a dilute aqueous solution of chiefly low molecular weight compounds, amongst which are mineral salts and organic acids. Since the electron micrograph is of an immature cell, many smaller vacuoles are present.

Physiologically, the most important part of the cell is the **cytoplasm**. In mature cells it forms a thin layer around the vacuole, with occasional strands traversing it. The cytoplasm is separated from the vacuole by a definite membrane, the **tonoplast**. Another membrane, the **plasmalemma**, bounds the outer cytoplasmic surface, and is in contact with the wall. Various types of structures are visible within the cytoplasm. The most important of these is the **nucleus**, usually an approximately spherical or sometimes disc-shaped body, bounded by a **nuclear membrane**, which is believed to be minutely perforated. Within the nucleus, one or more clear, spherical **nucleoli** may be seen. **Mitochondria** are rod-shaped bodies, rarely exceeding 10μ in length, in which the oxidative reactions of respiration proceed. Usually, they

15

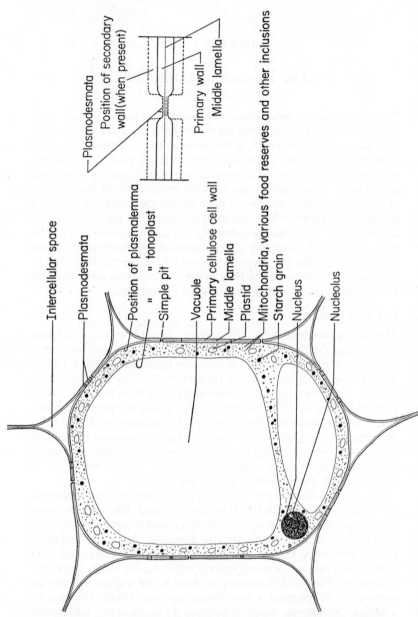

FIG. 4. Diagram of a parenchyma cell, showing structures which could be seen, given appropriate conditions, under the ordinary light microscope. The inset gives details of the construction of a simple pit.

can only be seen under the light microscope after special staining techniques. **Plastids** also occur widely. Like mitochondria, they are bounded by a membrane, and are of various shapes, but they differ in their internal structure, and in any given cell they are usually much larger, ranging up to 100μ in size. Some plastids, the **leucoplasts**, are colourless, and these frequently contain starch grains. **Chromoplasts** contain red, orange, or yellow pigments, and are abundant in many flowers and fruits. **Chloroplasts** are saucer- or lens-shaped plastids containing the green pigment chlorophyll, and in which the reactions of photosynthesis take place. The cytoplasm and its organelles possess great structural complexity at a level only revealed by the electron microscope. This is briefly discussed in Section 3 of this chapter.

The cell wall lies next to the plasmalemma. It is composed chiefly of cellulose, which imparts some structural rigidity to the cell. In parenchyma cells, it is often a **primary wall** only. This means that it is the original, rather extensible wall laid down whilst the cell was actually growing, and that little or no additional material has been deposited since. Sometimes, however, a considerable amount of new cellulose is added on the inside, after completion of cell expansion, to constitute a **secondary wall**. In other types of cells, substances such as lignin or suberin may also be incorporated into the secondary wall. The first formed, and hence the oldest layer of the primary wall, is the **middle lamella**. This very thin layer of protopectin effectively cements the walls of two contiguous cells. Often, cells do not interlock completely, leaving **intercellular spaces**. These are normally gas-filled and provide an 'internal atmosphere' in which diffusion of gases to and from the living cells takes place. This system is most strongly developed in the mesophyll of leaves, and in all parts of aquatic plants. The shape of each cell is modified by the presence of its neighbours, and each may bear a dozen or more flattened faces, each face having varying numbers of sides.

There are usually many **simple pits** present in the wall. These are well-defined regions where the wall abruptly becomes very thin. Normally, the corresponding region of the adjacent cell is similarly modified, and the two together constitute a **pit pair**. The pit membrane, details of which are not easily discernible under the light microscope in unstained parenchyma cells, consists of the middle lamella plus the very thin parts of the two primary walls. If a secondary wall forms, it does so only over the non-pitted part, so that the pits deepen. **Plasmodesmata** are thin strands of cytoplasm which pass through the cell wall, so connecting adjacent protoplasts. Although they may occur in any part of the wall, they are concentrated in pit membranes. They are more prominent in young cells. Again, plasmodesmata cannot often be seen under the light microscope, but several prominent ones are shown in Plate I. The significance of pits and plasmodesmata is not known, but it is tempting to suppose that they serve to facilitate passage of metabolites between cells, within a protoplasmic continuum.

2. The Cell Wall

Cellulose is a carbohydrate, whose molecules each consist of many hundreds of cellobiose units joined end to end, producing a linear structure of immense length and very high (though unknown) molecular weight. The thread-like molecular chains are aggregated together into ribbon-shaped structures called **microfibrils**, about 250Å wide, and visible only under the electron microscope. The formation of microfibrils is facilitated by the existence of copious hydrogen bonds between hydrogen atoms and oxygen atoms on adjacent molecular chains, so binding the chains together. Microfibrils are themselves grouped together into much larger **macrofibrils**, which are sometimes visible under the light microscope. Within each microfibril there

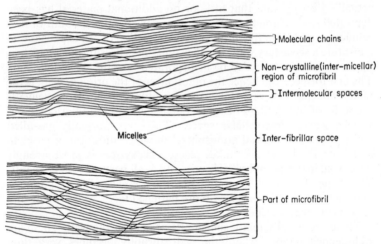

Molecular chains

Non–crystalline(inter–micellar) region of microfibril

Intermolecular spaces

Micelles

Inter–fibrillar space

Part of microfibril

FIG. 5. Diagram of parts of two cellulose microfibrils, showing the relationships between molecular chains, microfibrils, and micelles, in plant cell walls.

are spaces between the molecular chains, and, at a more gross level, there are spaces between the microfibrils themselves. These intermolecular and interfibrillar spaces are partly occupied by additional structural encrusting materials, chiefly hemicelluloses and pectic compounds, but one of the most important features is that, due to imbibitional and capillary effects, the spaces are largely water-filled. Thus, the cell wall is heavily hydrated. In primary walls water may account for as much as 70 per cent of the volume. Fig. 5 illustrates the relationship between microfibrils and molecular chains. **Micelles** are regions where the molecular chains lie very nearly parallel to one another, giving regions where, due to the orderly array of cellobiose units resulting in turn in a very regular arrangement of atoms, the cellulose is essentially crystalline in character. Each cellulose molecule is long enough to participate in the formation of several micelles, which are usually about 500Å long. In primary walls, the microfibrils, whilst still showing micelles, are not regularly arranged with respect to each other, resulting in a large amount of interfibrillar space. This makes it easy to understand why primary walls are so plastic and extensible. In secondary walls, on the other hand, the microfibrils are more closely parallel, leading to much more efficient packing, and leaving much less room for water between them.

Most analyses of primary walls indicate the presence of a considerable proportion of protein (usually between 10 and 20 per cent dry weight). This may well be due to permeation of the primary wall by the outer layers of the cytoplasm, with which it is in intimate contact. It does not imply the participation of protein in the essential construction of the cell wall.

3. The Nature of Protoplasm

Protoplasm is the material of which both nucleus and cytoplasm are composed. It is the seat of an enormous range of biochemical reactions, which can be divided into distinct groups such as protein synthesis, photosynthesis and respiration. Whilst there are important links between such pathways, each nevertheless requires different raw materials, and yields separate products. The individual reactions composing each pathway usually require a specific enzyme. For example, more than twenty such enzyme-controlled stages are required before a molecule of glucose is finally oxidized to water and carbon dioxide during respiration. Here, energy is made available to the cell, whilst in processes like protein synthesis and salt uptake energy is used. In such a highly complex situation it is not surprising that different sets of reactions, which may require different materials or conditions, and which travel in opposite directions energetically, are localized in different regions of a cell. Thus, for example, photosynthetic reactions proceed within chloroplasts, and respiratory reactions within the mitochondria. Biochemical pathways are, however, less isolated from one another chemically than spatially. Certain freely diffusible substances such as, for example, adenosine phosphates and certain co-enzymes, take part in many pathways, and may be thought of as existing in a common 'metabolic pool', for which the various processes compete.

Before discussing further the fine structure of protoplasm, it will be helpful to review some of its more important properties.

(a) **Viscosity.** Even within different parts of one cell, the viscosity of protoplasm may vary considerably. In the sol form, Brownian movement can be demonstrated, and it will flow freely, although its viscosity is always at least several times greater than that of water. When in this state, protoplasm often appears to circulate round the cell, carrying with it the mitochondria, starch grains and other inclusions. This movement is called cyclosis, and it can readily be observed in fresh *Elodea* cells mounted in a drop of water on a barely warm slide. The rate of movement is less than $\frac{1}{10}$ mm per second, but it is certainly possible that it assists in the distribution of metabolic substances within the cell. Rapid gelation can occur, when Brownian movement ceases, and the whole tends to solidify. Gelation occurs particularly in response to alterations in temperature or pH, or to the addition of certain reagents. Thixotropy (see p. 5) has also been observed. In highly active cells, the sol form tends to be found, whereas gels are encountered mainly in such quiescent cells as those of dormant seeds or spores. The highly hydrated state of active protoplasm is doubtless essential for the rapid diffusion of metabolites.

Protoplasm behaves in a 'non-Newtonian' manner when its rate of flow under varying pressures is measured. True liquids show direct proportionality between the pressure applied and the rate of flow, whereas protoplasm deviates markedly from such 'Newtonian' behaviour. This indicates the presence of a definite framework of molecules.

(b) **Elasticity.** It has been possible to micromanipulate from some plant cells, threads of protoplasm which quickly spring back when released. This again suggests some kind of molecular framework which can recover after being stretched.

(c) **Optical properties.** When protoplasm is flowing in a particular direction, and a beam of polarized light is passed through it, the plane of polarization is rotated. This property is called birefringence, and it should be noted that again this is characteristic of substances which possess a regular arrangement of molecules, being best developed in the case of crystalline substances. This 'birefringence of flow' of protoplasm is believed to be due to the lining-up of long molecular chains parallel to the direction of flow.

(d) **Imbibition.** If dry pea seeds are placed in a medicine bottle, and the bottle is topped up with water and securely fastened, the glass is liable to be shattered within a few hours. This results from the imbibition of water by the protoplasmic gel, bringing about swelling of the seed. After solation of the protoplasm, the physiological activities of germination ensue. We have already seen that imbibition is characteristic of many other colloidal gels (see p. 6).

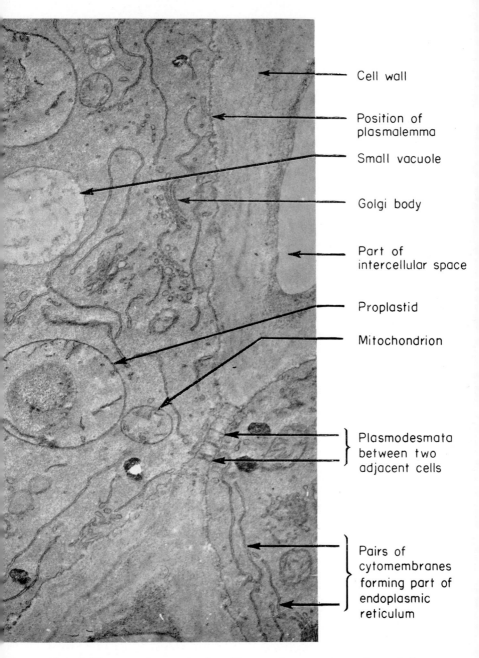

- Cell wall
- Position of plasmalemma
- Small vacuole
- Golgi body
- Part of intercellular space
- Proplastid
- Mitochondrion
- } Plasmodesmata between two adjacent cells
- } Pairs of cytomembranes forming part of endoplasmic reticulum

Plate I. Electron micrograph of small parts of two meristematic cortical cells from root apex of broad bean (×7500). (*Photo by* Dr B. E. Juniper.)

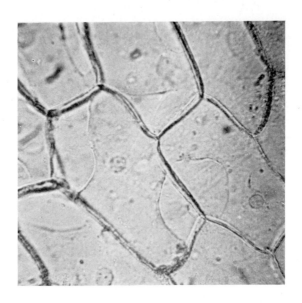

Plate II. (*a*) Plasmolysed cells from onion bulb scale epidermis; (*b*) 'Leaf skeleton' of a dicotyledon, obtained by allowing the soft parts of the leaf to decay, whilst all but the finest vascular traces remain.

(e) **Coagulation.** Like most hydrophilic colloids, protoplasm is stable to the addition of very low concentrations of electrolytes, but higher concentrations bring about coagulation and death. If, however, the solution contains a balanced mixture of mono-, di- and trivalent ions, the effect is much less destructive. This illustrates the well-known principle of ion-antagonism. Coagulation is also brought about by temperatures much above 45° C, by freezing, or by ionizing radiations. It is due to denaturation of the protoplasmic proteins. The resistance of protoplasm to coagulation is much greater if the proportion of water it contains is small, as in heat-resistant bacterial and fungal spores.

(f) **Chemical analysis.** An accurate analysis is very difficult to perform, one reason for this being the difficulties in obtaining specimens of protoplasm entirely free from other cell constituents.

The amount of water present is very variable. In normally active cells, the proportion seems to be of the order of 90 per cent, whereas in cases where physiological activity is low, the content may be as low as 10 per cent.

The indications are that approximately 65 per cent of the dry weight consists of proteins and amino-acids, about 12 per cent of lipid (fatty) material, and about 15 per cent of simple sugars. The remainder is accounted for by small quantities of numerous other organic compounds, with some mineral matter. The various constituents are not distributed uniformly. The bulk of the lipid fraction, for example, is located in mitochondria and plastids. Lipids are a complex assortment of compounds, and the only simple property which they share is that of solubility in the fat solvents, such as chloroform, benzene and acetone. There are three principal types. The **true fats** (e.g. coconut oil) are esters of fatty acids with glycerol, and are probably freely dispersed in the form of droplets, to form a colloidal emulsion. The **phospholipids** (e.g. lecithin) are compounds of fatty acids and phosphoric acid. The **sterols** (e.g. ergosterol) are complex ring compounds. Phospholipids and sterols are believed by many to take a more definite part in forming the structural basis of protoplasm than the true fats.

Over the years, a picture of protoplasm as a colloidal system of at least three phases has emerged. According to this, the largest component is a medium made up of a true aqueous solution of a wide variety of organic and inorganic solutes. Dispersed in this is an oily phase, consisting of minute lipid droplets, giving to protoplasm the properties of a colloidal emulsion. Finally, there is some kind of framework formed by joined protein molecules. Several types of chemical bonds of varying strengths, including hydrogen bonds, may join these molecules, the strengths varying with the conditions, sometimes allowing fluidity, but at other times imparting a much more rigid structure. It is thought that the protein chains each take the form of a helix, and that they can form fibrils by twisting together like the strands of a rope. When stretched, the helices open out like a spring, giving considerable elasticity. Protein molecules are also folded in a complex manner.

Recently, electron microscope studies have suggested that, although fibrils of the type already mentioned almost certainly exist in protoplasm, another rather more elaborate type of organization is widespread. The idea here is that a system of membranes exists, which are arranged approximately parallel with one another and with the cell surface. These **cytomembranes** have now been observed many times in electron microscope studies, and a few can be seen in Plate I on p. 20. They are arranged in pairs, so that each pair encloses a fluid-filled channel. Together, the cytomembranes make up what is called the **endoplasmic reticulum**. Associated with the membranes, on the side away from the channel, are usually numerous small spheres (not visible in Plate I) called **ribosomes**. Other ribosomes lie free in the more fluid phase. These bodies appear to be the chief sites of cell protein synthesis. The extent to which the endoplasmic reticulum is developed is very variable. The Golgi bodies are specialized local regions of the endoplasmic reticulum whose precise function is unknown, though they appear to be concerned with some kind of secretion.

We can thus visualize protoplasm as a system in which proteins may assume the form of fibrils, or take part in the formation of membranes. No definite information is available as to the molecular structure of cytomembranes, but this could well be very similar to that of the plasmalemma and tonoplast, which is discussed below. Indeed, some workers have suggested that they may be invaginations of these boundaries.

The structural basis of the tonoplast and plasmalemma is, in all probability, a bimolecular layer of phospholipids, A phospholipid is a long-chain molecule, one end of which has a strong affinity for water, and is said to be hydrophilic or polar. The opposite end tends to be repelled from water, and consists only of carbon and hydrogen atoms. It tends to attract similar hydrocarbon groups, and is called lipophilic, or non-polar. These molecules, therefore, tend to form layers, two molecules in thickness, with the lipophilic ends directed inwards towards one another, and the polar or hydrophilic groups on the outside. Since the polar groups are charged, they can attract oppositely charged parts of protein molecules, and the final result is a bimolecular phospholipid layer, plastered together with a layer of protein on either side. There are very probably various sizes of pores present also. Fig. 6 shows, diagrammatically, the structure postulated by Professor Danielli. The essentials of this picture were built up as long ago as

1940, on the basis of indirect observation and calculation, and Professor Danielli was able to suggest that the membranes, if so constructed, would be about 80Å, or 8mμ, in thickness. Electron micrographs of cytoplasmic membranes have shown that each member of a pair appears as two dense regions, each about 20Å thick, which could represent the protein layers. Between this is a much less dense layer, 35Å thick, corresponding to the lipid component. This total thickness of about 75Å strikingly supports the Danielli conception.

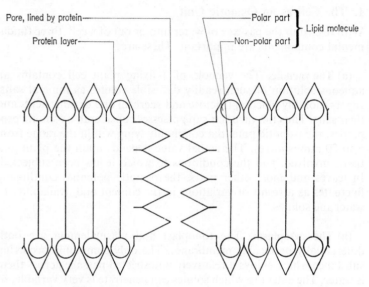

Fig. 6. Approximate representation of the possible structure of cell membranes (Danielli).

So far as the organelles are concerned, it has been shown quite conclusively that the mitochondria and chloroplasts have a complex membranous internal structure. A sectioned mitochondrion, for example, is seen in electron microscope studies to consist of a vesicle bounded by a double membrane. The inner of these appears to be invaginated many times, to give a complex internal arrangement. Chloroplasts are constructed along somewhat similar lines. On this basis, both types of structure can be regarded as rather specialized regions of the cytomembrane system.

CHAPTER THREE

Water Relationships of Cells and Tissues

1. The Cell as an Osmotic Unit

With regard to the passage of water into or out of a cell, three fundamental components are important. These are:

(a) **The vacuole.** The vacuole of a living plant cell contains an aqueous solution of such readily diffusible solutes as mineral salts, sugars (notably glucose, fructose and sucrose) and organic acids and their salts. Thus the vacuolar sap possesses considerable osmotic properties, the osmotic potential commonly lying within the range from 5 to 20 atmospheres. The actual value depends upon the plant and tissue involved, and the conditions to which it has been subjected. In leaves and most other parts, the osmotic potential continually fluctuates as a result of variations in the content and availability of water and solutes.

(b) **The cytoplasm.** The tonoplast and plasmalemma are both differentially permeable membranes. The only commonly occurring substance which enjoys a relatively unrestricted passage across them is water. The extent to which solutes can penetrate is very variable, so that few useful generalizations can be made. Although pores exist in the membranes, through which passage presumably can take place, the permeability characteristics do not seem to be due chiefly to microsieve effects. For example, fatty compounds penetrate more readily than other molecules of comparable size, possibly because they can dissolve in the lipid part of the membrane and so pass across it. By contrast, particles as small as inorganic ions penetrate with greater difficulty. Factors such as age, pH, temperature, and the presence or absence of certain ions profoundly affect the permeability of cell membranes to different solutes. Clearly, complicated mechanisms are involved, and about these little is known. It seems likely that the plasmalemma and tonoplast differ in their permeability, the latter generally presenting the more formidable barrier. Once inside the cytoplasm, solutes pass freely within its groundwork, but the membranes surrounding such organelles as mitochondria and chloroplasts are again differentially permeable. This isolates them to some extent, and so assists these specialized regions to carry out their separate functions. It is worth pointing out here that water and solutes may travel from one protoplast to the next, via plasmodesmata, without having to pass through the plasmalemma of either cell, though the extent to which this actually takes place is not known. It should be noted that only in the living state are the cytoplasmic membranes differentially permeable.

In order to demonstrate how the differential permeability of cell membranes may be affected by various factors, the following procedure may be adopted. Strips of fresh, well washed, beetroot tissue about 5 cm in length are accurately measured and placed in tubes containing molar sucrose solution, ethyl alcohol and distilled water respectively. After half an hour, the liquids are examined, and the strips removed and re-measured. The strips immersed in the strong sucrose solution are found to have shrunk, and the solution to have remained clear, since only water has escaped by osmosis. The strips placed in alcohol have shrunken, and the medium is reddened, due to the outward diffusion of the large anthocyanin molecules and water from the vacuole, through the cytoplasm. This is because of the denaturation of the cytoplasmic membranes, which are rendered permeable. It should be noted that when the differential permeability of the cytoplasm is destroyed, the cells cease to have osmotic properties, and the cell walls are able to return to an unstretched state. This results in a bulk physical expulsion of some of the vacuolar sap, in addition to the diffusion process. The effect is a more rapid reddening of the external solution than would be the case if only simple diffusion of anthocyanin molecules were to take place. The strips placed in pure water will have increased slightly in length, due to endosmosis, the medium remaining clear. If the strips are now replaced in the sucrose solution and the distilled water, and the tubes heated, in both cases the external solution becomes pigmented when the temperature reaches about 50° C, corresponding to the denaturation of the cytoplasmic proteins at the high temperature.

It is interesting to reflect that if the cytoplasmic membranes did not restrict the passage of solutes, plants would be unable to accumulate their essential metabolites. If diffusion were to take place freely, dissolved substances would pass from the relatively highly concentrated solution in the cell vacuoles into the dilute soil solution, with which the roots are in intimate contact. Such leakage which does occur is on a minute scale, although it is sufficient to attract to the immediate vicinity of the root large populations of micro-organisms, which feed on these substances and on sloughed-off root tissue. Small amounts of amino-acids and sugars may be lost from the root, and the rhizosphere population of micro-organisms is many times denser than in the soil at large.

It follows that if ions cannot easily diffuse into the soil from a plant, their uptake from the soil poses corresponding problems, especially since the absorption of ions must take place against a concentration gradient, that is, in the reverse direction to that in which diffusion would normally take place. Salt uptake is, therefore, an energy-consuming process. Considerable work has to be done in order to accumulate ions, and it is one of the most important cell activities which depends upon the energy made available by respiration. As such, it is quite different from, and largely independent of water uptake, which is essentially a passive physical process. Thus, salt uptake is profoundly affected by factors which alter the rate of metabolism, such as oxygen supply, and the presence of narcotics, whilst transpiration and water uptake are little affected. On the other hand, alterations in physical factors such as humidity, wind velocity and degree of stomatal opening, which have enormous effects on transpiration and water uptake, generally have little or no effect on the accumulation of ions. The working of ion-uptake processes is very imperfectly understood and the many postulated mechanisms, though interesting, are beyond the scope of this book.

(c) The cell wall. As was indicated in Chapter Two, this can be regarded as consisting of a basic scaffolding of cellulose, the spaces between which are occupied by varying amounts of other structural materials, and by water. These aqueous spaces in the walls of parenchyma cells are so extensive that even high molecular weight solutes can penetrate freely. This is not the case, however, in those cells where the cellulose has become impregnated with suberin or cutin, impermeable substances found notably in the cell walls of cork and epidermis respectively.

The other important property of cellulose is its slight elasticity, so that walls can stretch to allow some increase in the volume of the cell contents, whilst at the same time tending to return to the unstretched state.

2. Osmotic Forces in Living Cells

With the above discussion in mind, some of the forces which govern the flow of water within cells and tissues can now be examined. Consider the case where a freshly excised cube of beetroot or potato tissue is immersed in pure water. At once, osmosis begins, water passing into the vacuole of each cell through the cytoplasm and its membranes. (Some water will, of course, enter and remain within the cytoplasm itself, since this also contains osmotic substances, probably at different concentrations from those in the vacuole. However, since the cytoplasmic volume is small compared with the vacuole, it is permissible to regard the cytoplasm as a single thin membrane throughout this discussion.) The influx of water naturally causes the vacuole to enlarge, and it pushes outwards on the cytoplasm and cell wall with a force known as the **turgor pressure**. This leads to a stretching of the wall, and due to its elasticity, it tends to return to an unstretched state. Furthermore, when a group of cells is being considered, each cell, as it tends to expand, presses against, and is restrained by its neighbours. Thus there is an inwardly directed force placed on the vacuolar contents by the cell wall, due not only to the tendency for the stretched wall to regain its unstretched state, but also to the pressure from surrounding cells. This total force is called the **wall pressure**, and it will be seen that it acts in opposition to the turgor pressure, and is numerically equal to it when the cells stops expanding. A point is reached at which the inwardly directed wall pressure is sufficiently high to prevent further osmotic flow. The situation is comparable with that of the osmometer on p. 11. In the present case, the force preventing osmosis is due to the stretched cell wall and the pressure from surrounding cells, whereas in the model, it is due to the head of liquid in the apparatus. In either case, it is equal, by definition, to the osmotic potential of the now diluted solution, since in each case this is separated from pure water by a differentially permeable membrane. At this stage, then, there is no net flow of water in any direction.

The maximum force with which water can enter a cell is equal to the osmotic potential (or diffusion pressure deficit) of the solution composing the vacuolar sap. Under normal circumstances, however, this is opposed by the stretched cell wall and the pressure from surrounding cells, as outlined above, so that when cells are placed in pure water, the actual force with which water is taken up is the resultant of these two opposing effects. This net resultant force is called the diffusion pressure deficit of the cells.[1] The diffusion pressure deficit of a cell may thus be defined as **the force in atmospheres with which water enters a cell when placed in pure water.**

It will be seen that the diffusion pressure deficit of a cell is equal to the osmotic potential (or diffusion pressure deficit) of the solution composing the vacuolar sap, minus the wall pressure. This may be expressed in the form of a simple equation:

D.P.D. $\quad=\quad$ O.P. $\quad-\quad$ W.P.

(diffusion pressure (osmotic potential (wall pressure
deficit of cell) of vacuolar sap) of cell)

This relationship is a highly important one, to which reference will be

---

[1] The terms 'suction pressure' and 'suction force' are sometimes employed as alternatives to 'diffusion pressure deficit'; the reader should clearly understand that these three terms have the same meaning when applied to cells.

made many times in this book. The reader should make certain that he understands its meaning and mode of derivation before proceeding further with this chapter.

Suppose now that a tissue is bathed not by pure water, but by a solution of an osmotically active substance such as sucrose. Here the solution itself has a diffusion pressure deficit. In such a case the direction in which water will flow will be determined by whether the cell or the external solution possesses the greater D.P.D. If the solution is sufficiently concentrated, its D.P.D. will be greater than that of the cell, and water will pass out. If, on the other hand, only a weak solution is involved, water may be absorbed, though clearly not with so great a force as when the external medium is pure water. In other words, the presence of solutes externally, brings about a force in addition to the wall pressure of the cells, helping to prevent an influx of water into the tissue.

Since the maximum force with which water can ever enter a given cell at any time is attained only when the external medium is pure water, it follows that under these latter conditions, the maximum amount of water enters, and the cell becomes as fully distended as it can be. At this point the cell is said to be **fully turgid**, or to be in a state of **full turgor**.

3. Plasmolysis

It was stated above that the difference in diffusion pressure deficits between a cell and its surroundings is the force which determines whether any net flow of water takes place between them. In order to clarify this point, and to examine what happens in certain extreme cases, some hypothetical examples will be taken in which separate groups of cells are placed in different media whose osmotic potentials (or D.P.D.s) are 0, 5, 10, 15 and 20 atmospheres respectively. The cells will be assumed to have, initially, vacuolar osmotic potentials of 15 atmospheres, wall pressures of 10 atmospheres, and hence D.P.D.s of 5 atmospheres. For simplicity, any changes in the concentration of vacuolar sap due to entry or loss of water will be neglected for the moment. The reader will realize that some such changes must occur, but they are small, and would cause no significant differences to the events as outlined below.

(a) **External O.P. (or D.P.D.)** = 0. Since the D.P.D. of the external solution is zero, and that of the cells is, initially, 5 atmospheres, water will flow into the cells with a force of 5 atmospheres. The cells will expand, and the wall pressure increase, but when it reaches 15 atmospheres (since D.P.D. = O.P. — W.P.) the D.P.D. of the cells at this point will be zero, and equal to that of the external medium (0 = 15 — 15). Thus there will be no further net flow. Since the external medium is pure water, the cells will be at their maximum volume, and also be at full turgor.

(b) **External O.P. (or D.P.D.) = 5.** Since in this case the diffusion pressure deficits of the cells and the external solution are equal, no net flow of water takes place, and the volumes of the cells remain unchanged.

(c) **External O.P. (or D.P.D.) = 10.** The external D.P.D. this time exceeds that of the cells by 5 atmospheres, so that in this case water will pass out, the cells shrink, and the wall pressure fall. When the wall pressure reaches 5 atmospheres, the cell D.P.D. will be equal to that of the external medium, and shrinkage will cease (10 = 15 — 5).

(d) **External O.P. (or D.P.D.) = 15.** Here the external D.P.D. exceeds that of the cell by 10 atmospheres, so that water will pass out with this force. When the wall pressure reaches zero, the D.P.D. of the cell will be just equal to that of the external solution, and so the flow will cease (15 = 15 − 0). In this case, the cell wall will not be in the stretched state when equilibrium is reached.

(e) **External O.P. (or D.P.D.) = 20.** The external D.P.D. exceeds that of the cell by 15 atmospheres. When the cell has shrunk to such an extent that the wall pressure is nil (as in (d)) the D.P.D. of the cell is still 5 atmospheres less than that of the external medium. The cell wall cannot shrink further, but the only way in which equilibrium can be brought about is by the continued removal of water from the vacuole. Thus the cytoplasm shrinks away from the cell wall, and water continues to pass from the vacuole until its contents are sufficiently concentrated to exert a D.P.D. equal to that of the external medium, or, in other words, until the O.P. (or D.P.D.) of the contents rises to 20 atmospheres. When the protoplast shrinks away from the walls, the cell is said to be **plasmolysed**. Some of the external medium, called the plasmolyticum, enters the space between the cytoplasm and the cell wall. The whole phenomenon is called **plasmolysis**.

The results of the five treatments are shown very diagrammatically in Fig. 7. In example (d), it was indicated that the abolition of the wall pressure, brought about by the reduced volume of the vacuole, was just sufficient to bring about equilibrium without plasmolysis taking place. In actual fact, however, the wall pressure is not quite abolished when equilibrium is attained in this solution, since the vacuolar sap becomes slightly concentrated by the loss of water. Suppose that the internal osmotic potential rose from 15 to 16 atmospheres in this way. At equilibrium, a wall pressure of 1 atmosphere would be maintained (15 = 16 − 1). Thus an external O.P. of 16 atmospheres would be needed to completely abolish the wall pressure (16 = 16 − 0).

When the wall pressure of a cell is zero. the cell is said to be in a state of **incipient plasmolysis**. Clearly, at this point, the O.P. (or D.P.D.) of the almost plasmolysed cell is equal to that of the external solution, and any increase in the latter would bring about plasmolysis. Photomicrographs of plasmolysed cells from the upper epidermis of an inner

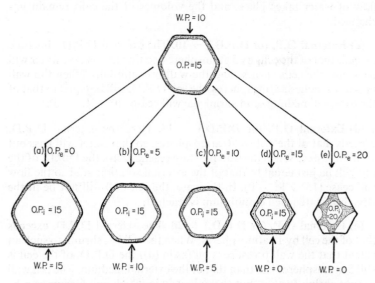

FIG. 7. Diagram to illustrate the expected change taking place in a single parenchyma cell removed from a tissue and placed in external solutions of various osmotic potentials. Except in (*d*) changes in vacuolar sap concentration are ignored. The differences in relative cell size are greatly exaggerated O.P.$_e$ is the osmotic potential of external solution, O.P.$_i$ the osmotic potential of vacuolar sap, and W.P. the wall pressure. Note that in each case at equilibrium, O.P.$_i$ = W.P.

scale of an onion are shown in Plate IIa. Sometimes, the contracted protoplast assumes the form of a smooth cylinder with rounded ends, especially if plasmolysis is carried out slowly. Often, however, it withdraws from the cell wall with difficulty, and parts may remain attached to it, either in the form of strands, or sometimes as quite large portions, which break away from the main bulk. This suggests that the protoplasm in some cases at least, may penetrate some distance into the actual meshwork of the primary cell wall, instead of being so sharply delimited from it as it suggested by microscopic observation.

If plasmolysed cells are transferred from the plasmolyticum into water, full turgor is regained. This **deplasmolysis**, or recovery, is due to an influx into osmotic the vacuole. In order for deplasmolysis to take place, it is not essential for the cells to be transferred into pure water. Any solution whose osmotic potential is equal to, or less than, the osmotic potential of the vacuolar contents in the original unplasmolysed cells will suffice, although of course the cell will not regain *full* turgor unless pure water is used.

Effects resembling the appearance of plasmolysed cells may be brought about by substances injurious to the cytoplasm, such as strong solutions of inorganic salts, particularly those containing monovalent ions. Such substances cause coagulation of the cytoplasm, the protoplast often shrinking to the middle of the cell. In such cases, when the 'plasmolysed' cells are returned to water, no recovery occurs, since the cytoplasmic membranes are no longer differentially permeable, and so cannot bring about osmosis.

It was pointed out at the beginning of this present chapter that different solutes penetrate the cytoplasmic membranes to varying extents, and at different rates. If cells are bathed in a hypertonic solution of a substance whose molecules slowly penetrate the cytoplasm, plasmolysis takes place, only to be followed by spontaneous recovery some time later. With *Spirogyra* filaments, immersed in a 5 per cent glycerol solution, plasmolysis usually proceeds within about twenty minutes, and after twenty-four hours, turgidity has been regained, although the response varies between species, and with the season. In the plasmolysed condition, the sap in the contracted protoplast is isotonic with the plasmolyticum. The osmotic potential of the latter is entirely due to the glycerol it contains, whereas that of the former is due mainly to the many types of solutes normally present in the cell, plus the very small amount of glycerol which has had time to penetrate. Since, however, there is a diffusion pressure gradient of glycerol, molecules of this compound will slowly pass across the protoplast, and the concentration of glycerol on each side will become equalized. As a result, the total osmotic potential of the vacuolar sap begins to exceed that of the external medium, and water returns to the vacuole, which expands to its former size.

4. The Evaluation of Osmotic Quantities

Simple, well-tried methods are available for the determination of the D.P.D. and O.P. of plant tissues. These values are useful physiological data, and help in understanding, for example, the effects of different storage conditions on vegetable and fruit crops.

(a) **D.P.D.** The principle used here is that if the D.P.D. of a tissue is greater than that of a surrounding aqueous medium (as in (a) and (b) p. 28) water is absorbed, the cells expand, and the tissue increases both in volume and weight. Conversely, if the D.P.D. of the tissue is less than that of the medium, the dimensions will decrease ((d) and

(e) p. 29). Only if the two D.P.D.s are equal will there be no change. A series of sucrose or potassium nitrate solutions of known concentrations is prepared, and a sample of the freshly-cut and measured tissue is immersed in each solution. After a suitable period (half an hour, or longer, depending upon the bulk of the test material) the tissue is removed and re-measured.

The method is suitable for strips of such materials as flower petals, leaves, or storage organs. The strips should measure about 5 cm × 5 mm, and, in the case of storage organs, should be about 2 mm in thickness. The lengths of one edge of each strip are accurately measured, and two strips are then placed in each solution, contained in a covered Petri dish to prevent evaporation. The measured edges should all be placed in one direction, so as to facilitate identification. A series of ten concentrations of sucrose solution between about 0.1 and 0.5 molar is appropriate for many tissues, but it is preferable to carry out a preliminary trial experiment to ascertain the best range for each particular case. At the end of the experimental period, the strips are removed, and the same edges re-measured.

If the weighing method is adopted, cylinders of about 1 cm diameter of the storage organ are removed with a cork borer, and discs 1–2 mm thick are sliced from this with a razor. The discs are carefully blotted, weighed in groups of ten, and each group is placed in a separate solution. At the end, they are removed, carefully blotted, and re-weighed. Weighings are best carried out in closed phials to avoid evaporation losses. The blotting procedure should be standardized – for example, by allowing the paper to remain in light contact with the discs for five seconds.

In either case, care must be taken to exclude, as far as possible, corky or vascular tissue, which could hinder the swelling or shrinkage process. A curve is drawn to show the relationship between the **percentage** change in length or weight, and the osmotic potential of the external medium. The O.P. of that solution which would cause no change in dimensions is determined from the graph, and this is equal to the average D.P.D. of the cells making up the tissue. It is desirable that the information used in the construction of the curve should represent the average results of as many replicates as possible. In a class experiment, of course, these may be performed simultaneously.

A popular subject for experiments relating to the D.P.D. of cells is provided by the scape (flower stalk) of the dandelion plant. Pieces of the scape, about 4 cm long, are cut into four longitudinal quadrants. Immediately, an outward bending takes place, due to the release of tissue tensions (see p. 39). A number of strips are prepared, and from them are selected a dozen or so whose curvatures are about the same. Two are kept in a closed tube as standards, and of the remainder, two are placed in each of a series of sucrose solutions between the range

0.25–0.05 molar. If the O.P. (D.P.D.) of the external solution exceeds the D.P.D. of the parenchyma cells, these lose water and the curvature lessens, but if the opposite situation exists, the strips become even more coiled, in some cases in a similar manner to a clock-spring. If, however, the curvature does not alter, the D.P.D. of the parenchyma cells is equal to that of the medium. The method is useful for the demonstration of osmotic effects. The material is usually readily available, and the curvature changes are rapid and spectacular. It is, however, hard to get a really accurate measurement of the D.P.D. of the tissue, because, unless one is especially fortunate, there is usually some change in curvature in all the solutions.

(b) **O.P.** Two methods are widely used. One of these makes use of the fact that the freezing point of an aqueous solution depends upon its concentration, as also, of course, does its osmotic potential. The relationship between the freezing point and the osmotic potential of a solution is given by the equation O.P. $= 12.04 \times$ freezing point. If, therefore, the freezing point of vacuolar sap can be found, so also can its osmotic potential. The major difficulty is that of obtaining sufficiently pure sap samples. This can be accomplished in the case of the green alga *Nitella*, in certain species of which single cells of the main, uniseriate, filament reach several centimetres in length (up to 25 cm in *N. cernua*). Here, the end of the cell is cut off, and some sap withdrawn, using a micropipette. Other types of tissue, such as beet, are first frozen to render the protoplast permeable, allowed to thaw, and then pressed to extract the sap. This method is unsatisfactory in that contamination from cytoplasmic components is unavoidable. Determinations of O.P. by the freezing point method are termed **cryoscopic methods**.

The other principal method used in determinations of O.P. is known as the **plasmometric method**. This depends upon the fact that, when cells are in a state of incipient plasmolysis (see p. 30) the O.P. of the vacuolar sap is equal to that of the external solution. The method is only suitable for one-cell-thick tissues, such as epidermal strips of a wide variety of leaves or onion bulb scales, algal filaments, or thin, washed slices of beetroot or similar material. The observations are much easier if cells with pigmented vacuolar sap are employed, and epidermal strips from the petiole of early rhubarb are often satisfactory. The staminal hairs of *Tradescantia* are particularly favourite material for observing plasmolysis, as they are uniseriate filaments with a purplish vacuolar sap. A species such as *T. paludosa* is easy to grow and, if maintained in a greenhouse all the year round, will flower prolifically. All these tissues are delicate, and careful handling is essential.

A small piece of the tissue is placed in each of a series of sucrose solutions, using the same range as in the above experiments with strips or discs, contained in covered watch glasses. Sometimes, the vessels containing the material are placed in a vacuum desiccator, which is slowly evacuated, to remove intercellular air. The vacuum is then released, and the spaces become injected with the fluid. This treatment, which is designed to ensure thorough penetration, is not, however, generally necessary or desirable.

At the end of half an hour, each piece of tissue is carefully mounted on a slide, in a drop of the same solution, and a total of up to a hundred living, intact cells is counted in each case, noting the number of plasmolysed and unplasmolysed cells. Several different fields of view will be necessary to include a sufficient number of cells. When the counts are complete, a curve is drawn to show the relationship between the percentage of cells plasmolysed and the O.P. of the solution. The external O.P. which corresponds to 50 per cent plasmolysed cells is determined from this curve.

At this point, a cell whose O.P. is equal to the average O.P. of all the cells in the tissue, will be in a state of incipient plasmolysis, and at this point its O.P. is equal to that of the medium. The quantity determined in this way is, then, the O.P. of an average cell when in the non-turgid state. When in the original turgid state, the value would be expected to be a little less than this, because, as a cell approaches incipient plasmolysis, its contents become slightly concentrated, due to loss of water from the vacuole.

The method described above is inclined to be laborious, but in a class experiment the work may be shared, each student dealing with only two or three solutions. Even so, results will be more reliable if several replicates of each treatment can be made.

5. Water Uptake by Non-Osmotic Means

So far, attention has been focused upon osmosis as the driving force of water uptake. Although there is no doubt that osmotic mechanisms do account for the greater part of such processes, some further possible factors must now be considered.

(a) **Imbibitional uptake.** As has already been pointed out, protoplasm, like other colloidal materials, can imbibe considerable amounts of water, especially when in the gel form. This capacity is especially notable in the case of dry seeds, which absorb much more water than can be accounted for by the osmotic potential of the cell contents alone. Other examples of possible imbibitional effects are considered below.

The newly-formed cells at the apices of stems and roots are small, thin-walled, approximately isodiametric, and with little vacuolation. In the region slightly further behind, marked cell-elongation takes place, and a large vacuole begins to occupy most of the cell volume. In order for elongation and vacuolation to take place, much water is absorbed, due largely to imbibition by the dense cytoplasm of the young cells. The swelling which accompanies this absorption provides the principal driving force needed for cell enlargement. Thus, it is not surprising that growth is severely retarded when a strong water deficit is incurred by plants due to a pronounced excess of transpiration over absorption.

Many lichens can endure considerable degrees of desiccation for long periods, becoming dry and brittle. On wetting, they imbibe water, regenerate, and become swollen and gelatinous.

The cell walls of ordinary plants are mostly impregnated with water, and if these walls are in contact with air, as in the case of leaf mesophyll, water evaporates from them. The walls, however, remain moist, so facilitating necessary gaseous exhanges, a property which is due chiefly to imbibition of water from the cytoplasm and vacuole, aided by capillarity.

(b) The problem of 'active uptake'. It has often been observed that determinations of osmotic potential by the plasmometric method and by the cryoscopic method yield discrepant results. The value obtained by the former method generally exceeds that found by the latter by 2 to 3 atmospheres. These differences are not explicable on the basis of simple osmotic or imbibitional effects.

It has been suggested that a force in addition to osmosis is involved in pumping water into a cell, thus making plasmolysis more difficult than it would otherwise be, so that an excessively strong solution has to be used. This idea is strongly supported by the fact that water uptake has, in a variety of tissues, been found to be affected by the degree of metabolic activity, a lowered respiration rate being correlated with a decreased rate of water uptake, and vice versa. Such results tend to indicate that some water may be taken up actively, that is, by a mechanism entailing the expenditure of metabolic energy.

Another source of evidence for the idea of an active component of water uptake, is the observation that cells, transferred from a salt solution with which they are in equilibrium to a sucrose solution of equal osmotic potential, may begin to take up appreciable amounts of water, the change being reversible. The implication here is that the presence of the sugar enhances the metabolic activity of the cell through acting as a respiratory substrate, and stimulates an active component of water absorption.

Further evidence that has been cited in favour of active uptake comes from the fact that the addition of auxins to certain tissues such as portions of potato tubers placed in pure water increases the rate of water uptake, and, in some cases, stimulates respiration. Auxins are hormones which greatly increase the extension growth of plant cells, and it has been postulated that their mode of action might be to somehow enhance metabolism, thereby increasing an active component of water uptake, and causing the cell to expand. This suggestion is, however, not likely to be the correct explanation of auxin action.

Although there is a large amount of experimental evidence to show that increased metabolic activity does enhance water uptake, the basis for this correlation is quite unsolved. A strong body of opinion favours the notion that the relationship is an indirect one. The view here is that increased metabolic activity, by favouring the uptake of salts from the medium (a process known to be respiration-dependent) causes a rise in the osmotic potential of the cell contents, and so increases osmotic water uptake. In order to explain the increased rate of uptake caused by auxin added to potato tissue placed in *pure water*, the view is taken that auxins merely render the cell wall more plastic by loosening the bonding between the wall materials. With the consequent decrease in the wall's restraining forces (i.e. in the wall pressure) a cell would then expand and take up more water by osmotic means, whether any active component of water uptake is operative or not. At least two groups of workers, using techniques involving isotopically 'labelled' water, have, in recent years, produced very strong evidence in favour of this concept of the mode of action of auxins,[1] and this explanation is almost certainly the correct one, although the details of the actual mechanism by which the mechanical coherence of the cell wall materials is reduced are as yet unsolved.

Finally, in this section, mention must be made of another possible mechanism that might be involved in water uptake. It is known that water will diffuse through small pores in a membrane under the influence of a potential difference across the membrane. This migration of water due to an electric field is called **electro-osmosis**. Potential differences definitely exist in plant tissues, and these are thought to be maintained by the differential permeability of the cell membranes to certain anions and cations, so that an excess of positively or negatively charged particles is enabled to build up. Since potential differences are known to exist in the tissues, electro-osmosis almost certainly occurs, but owing to the minute potential differences involved, the effect must be very small. It is interesting to note, however, that for the maintenance of the potential differences, a metabolic pumping of ions would have to be kept up. In other words, electro-osmotic effects could conceivably explain, partly or wholly, the effect of metabolic activity on the rate of water uptake. Electro-osmosis has also been invoked as an explanation of the movement of the contents of phloem sieve tubes.

[1] Thimann & Samuel, Proc. Nat. Acad. Sci. **41**, 1029–1033 (1955). Ordin & Bonner, Plant Physiol. **31**, 53–57 (1956).

It should be emphasized that what has been written in this whole section refers essentially to isolated cells, tissues or organs. In the entire, actively transpiring plant, the passive forces of water uptake are so large as to completely overshadow any active component; indeed, it is difficult to demonstrate the latter under such conditions (see p. 100).

6. Movement of Water Across Tissues

Plants absorb water from the soil on a very large scale. It has been shown, for example, that during a hot day, a sunflower plant may absorb several pints of water, whilst the amount absorbed by a large birch tree is of the order of a hundred gallons. Although absorption takes place principally in the finer, young roots, virtually all the water finds its ways to other parts. Most passes to the leaves, before finally evaporating into the atmosphere. Clearly, cell-to-cell movement of water must take place on a large scale in plant tissues, and it is this kind of movement which will now be considered. This discussion will be limited to purely osmotic effects, for although some water can undoubtedly be taken up by, and moved through, tissues by metabolic means (see above), there is no doubt that, in intact actively transpiring plants at least, the effect is so overshadowed by purely passive, osmotic forces that it can be safely disregarded.

Fig. 8(a) represents, diagrammatically, a series of three adjacent parenchyma cells, such as exist in the cortex of a root, or the mesophyll of a leaf. For the sake of simplicity, all are supposed to possess, initially, equal osmotic potentials, wall pressures and diffusion pressure deficits. Suppose now that water is being lost from cell C, into the surroundings, D. This would happen if the D.P.D. here is greater than that of the cell, which would be the case if, for example, D were an intercellular air space. Alternatively, there might be cells at D in which sugars or other solutes are accumulating. In either case, water is lost from the walls of cell C, resulting in a flow from the cytoplasm and vacuole. This produces two effects. Firstly, the vacuolar sap becomes more concentrated, and secondly, the cell shrinks, so that the wall pressure falls. Reference to the equation D.P.D. = O.P. − W.P. (p. 27) shows that both these effects tend to increase the D.P.D. of cell C. This inevitably leads to the absorption of water first from the cell wall, then the cytoplasm, and finally the vacuole of cell B, whose D.P.D. increases in the same way. Cell A then becomes similarly affected. Thus a train of events is set up, indicated in Fig 8(a) by the dotted arrows, involving the absorption of water from each cell into another of higher D.P.D., the row of cells acting as a kind of wick. So long as water is freely available at the source (which might, for example, be a xylem element) the cells remain turgid as the flow continues. If the supply becomes restricted, however, turgor is lost,

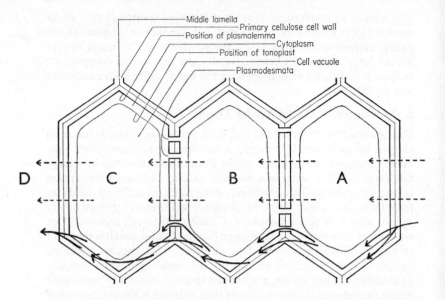

FIG. 8 (a). Diagram to illustrate alternative pathways of cell to cell water transfer. The broken arrows indicate the vacuolar pathway, the solid arrows indicate movement entirely within cells walls and cytoplasm.

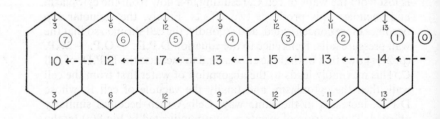

FIG. 8 (b). Diagram to illustrate transfer of water across a series of parenchyma cells, due to a D.P.D. gradient. The vacuolar osmotic potentials are shown in large type, wall pressures in small type, and the resultant D.P.D.s are encircled. A pure water source is assumed on the extreme right.

this situation corresponding to wilting. It will be seen that the movement of water is maintained by the existence of a D.P.D. gradient across the tissue.

It is appropriate to point out here that in order for cell-to-cell movement of water to take place, it is by no means essential for the osmotic potential of the recipient to exceed that of the donor. The driving force is the difference in diffusion pressure deficits of the cells, and not merely their relative osmotic potentials. Thus, in Fig. 8(b), water will flow in the direction shown, even though the osmotic potentials of the cells show wide fluctuations. This is because a high osmotic potential tends to be balanced by a high wall pressure. Variations of as much as 10 atmospheres between the osmotic potentials of the cells of particular tissues have often been recorded in experiments.

To conclude this section, a note of caution must be sounded against over-simplification of the mechanics of cell-to-cell transfer of water. In order for water to pass from cell A to cell C in the case considered above, it is not essential that all of it should enter the cell vacuoles. As water is lost from the cell wall and cytoplasm of C, the loss can be made good not only from the vacuole as already described, but also from the cytoplasm and cell wall of B. Such pathways are indicated in Fig. 8(a) by the solid arrows. Recent experiments, in which the path of 'labelled' water across tissues has been followed, suggest that it moves at the same *speed* through all the cell components. However, in view of the fact that most of the volume of a cell is due to the vacuole, it is almost certain that by far the largest *amount* of water travels via the vacuolar pathway.

7. The Role of Water in Support

When water is freely available to them, parenchyma cells are normally in a distended, turgid state. The extent to which the volume of each cell in a tissue can expand is, however, limited by the presence of surrounding cells. Thus the living cells of plant organs become packed tightly against one another in their natural tendency to expansion. Such a situation is the normal one in most herbaceous stems, roots and leaves, consisting as they do of a large proportion of parenchyma. In each case, the outer cells of the organ are much smaller and less extensible than the internal ones. Also, the epidermal surfaces of stems and leaves possess an almost inelastic cuticle. The result is that the forces due to the tendency of the internal cells to expand are nicely balanced by the forces with which the slightly stretched surface tissues are tending to regain their unstrained state. The situation may be compared with that of an inflated balloon, where the internal pressure is opposed by the stretched rubber.

That such forces exist in many young stems may be shown by

cutting a piece of the organ into four longitudinal quadrants, where-upon the strips immediately curve outwards. This is because the central cells have been freed from the restraint of the outer tissues. Stems of such common weeds as groundsel or sunspurge, or of marigold, or the dandelion scape referred to on p. 32 are suitable material for demonstrating these tissue tensions. Also, if the epidermis is stripped from a carefully measured piece of rhubarb petiole about 4 inches long, it will be found, on immediate re-measurement, to have contracted slightly.

Such a balance of forces imparts rigidity to plant organs, just as it does to an inflated football, balloon or tyre. The importance of turgor in this respect can be judged frpm the severe wilting which occurs when herbaceous plants are unable to absorb sufficient moisture to replace transpirational losses. This occurs especially in potted plants during hot summer days, or when a plant's root system has been damaged, as in the case of transplanted seedlings. Prolonged wilting can cause considerable damage, and the whole question is fully discussed in Chapter Seven. The leaves and stems of many plants native to arid regions possess strongly developed mechanical tissue, so that although the cells may lose turgor, visible wilting takes place much less readily than in ordinary plants.

Mechanical tissue is also the major means of support in older stems and roots, where large expanses of parenchyma do not normally occur. Here, the supporting tissue consists of heavily lignified cells, being either sclerenchyma, a tissue whose tensile strength is half that of wrought iron, or else the fibres, tracheids and, to some extent, the vessels of the xylem. The tremendous efficacy of lignified tissue may be judged from the huge loads borne by the trunks of foliage-laden trees, especially in high winds. Although a tree may be uprooted under such conditions, the trunk seldom snaps.

In the case of young growing stems, there is often a peripheral zone of collenchyma. The cell walls here are heavily reinforced with cellulose so that the tissue, whilst strong, is, unlike sclerenchyma, extensible, so as not to hinder growth. Since it allows some degree of bending, it is useful in climbing plants and in generally helping to withstand wind-buffeting. Collenchyma may also be found alongside the larger veins of leaves.

However, although lignified tissues and collenchyma are of un-doubted importance in the support of plants, there is no doubt that in nearly all herbaceous parts, cell turgor is by far the major factor.

REFERENCE

'Water relations of plant cells and tissues' – Kramer and Currier. Ann. Rev. Plant Phys. **1**. 265–284 (1950).

CHAPTER FOUR

The Path of Water

Generally speaking, water can travel in any direction through most plant structures, as determined by diffusion pressure gradients, but there are certain tissues and well-defined pathways along which the overwhelming proportion moves. Most eventually evaporates into the atmosphere from the leaves, only 1 or 2 per cent of the water absorbed being utilized for growth and general metabolism. As much as 2,000 grams of water may be lost from the leaves for each gram of dry weight increase. For the absorption and long-range conduction of water, special types of cells and tissues are needed. Also, special provisions are made to control the rate at which water is lost. In this chapter, the relevant structural features of ordinary plants are reviewed in relation to their role in the water factor.

The over-all path of water from the soil to the leaves is indicated in Fig. 27 (p. 93) and it may be conveniently considered under three main headings:

1 absorption, and lateral conduction across the young root tissue into the xylem;
2 vertical conduction within the xylem into the leaf;
3 passage across the leaf tissue, followed by evaporation into the atmosphere.

We are therefore concerned with the structure of:

1 the young root;
2 the xylem;
3 the leaf.

1. The Structure of Young Roots

Roots are both internally and externally more uniform in structure than stems. As a plant develops, its root system is constantly extending so that new sources of soil water may be exploited. The underground system so formed is typically highly branched, so presenting an enormous surface area of contact with the aqueous films around the soil particles.

At the extreme tip of each delicate young root is a zone of parenchyma cells, rich in starch grains, and usually called the **root cap.** Behind is a group of small, thin-walled cells with prominent nuclei,

41

but lacking large vacuoles. These cells are meristematic, constantly dividing to produce new tissue. As new cells are formed, they imbibe a great deal of water, lengthen markedly, and become vacuolated, that is, a very large vacuole is formed by the coalescence and enlargement of the numerous but much smaller ones present in the meristematic cells. There is no specialized water-conducting tissue in this region but cell-to-cell movement of water takes place, actuated by imbibitional or osmotic means. As a result of this production and elongation of new cells, the root tip is pushed forward. The root cap protects the meristem during this process, its tapering shape and mucilaginous character adapting it for penetration between the soil particles. Although the outer cells become sloughed off in the process, they are constantly replaced from below. Just after the commencement of cell elongation, differentiation into the distinct cell types which will be present in the mature root begins. The first vascular tissues to be formed are **protophloem** and **protoxylem**. Generally, protophloem, bringing supplies of the nutrients necessary for growth, is distinguishable before protoxylem. Considerable elongation continues during the early stages of tissue differentiation, but with the maturation of the first metaxylem elements, elongation practically ceases, since these elements are much more heavily lignified than those of the protoxylem, which means that they resist extension (see p. 55).

At this early stage, the outer root cells are all very thin-walled, and possess, at most, only a trace of cuticle, so that they absorb water freely. However, the absorptive capacity is vastly increased by the presence in nearly all plants of specialized structures known as **root hairs**. These are tubular extensions of certain of the outermost cells, and this layer is consequently called the **piliferous layer** (Fig. 10). Root hairs may reach a centimetre or more in length. Not only do they function for absorption, but they also ensure the firm anchorage of the region of the root just behind the apex, thus increasing the effectiveness with which the root tip pushes further into the soil. Most plants have a large safety margin as regards water absorptive capacity, for it appears that as much as one third of the root system may be in contact with very dry soil, or even removed altogether so long as the remainder is adequately watered, without causing serious harm. Under certain environmental conditions, however, such as those favouring a high rate of water loss, or when the soil is very dry, this safety margin may become important.

The cell walls of root hairs are very thin and, besides cellulose, contain a large proportion of pectic compounds in the form of a colloidal gel. This enables an intimate association with soil particles to be entered into, so that removal of these particles by careful washing is rendered difficult. For the same reason, most of the hairs are left behind in the soil when a seedling is uprooted for transplantation.

Next to the wall lies a thin lining of cytoplasm, in which the nucleus of the cell is situated. The cell vacuole extends into the hair, occupying most of its volume. In most cases, hairs appear over only a restricted region of the root. They do not develop on the rapidly elongating region, from which they would in any case be torn away. Neither do they occur in the older parts of the system, for here the outer cells have disrupted and fallen away, being replaced by a protective waterproof suberized layer of cells. Eventually, cork is formed. Thus root hairs remain functional for only a few days or weeks. In some exceptional cases, no suberization occurs and the hairs persist for a longer period.

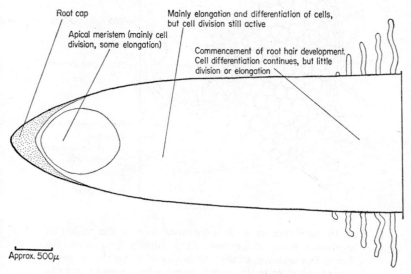

FIG. 9. The distribution of cell activities in a root tip (generalised and approximate).

From the preceding paragraphs it will be seen that four definite zones may be distinguished near the tip of roots:

1 the root cap;
2 a region where cell division and elongation predominate;
3 a region where elongation and differentiation predominate;
4 a root hair region, in which differentiation is still proceeding.

It should be noted that no sharp boundaries separate these zones; there is a steady transition from one to the next. In any case, their relative extents, especially that of the root hair zone, are very variable, depending not only upon the species of plant, but also upon the environmental conditions to which the plant has been subjected. As a very general guide, however, their approximate extents are shown in Fig. 9.

A common type of internal root structure is shown in Fig. 10. The

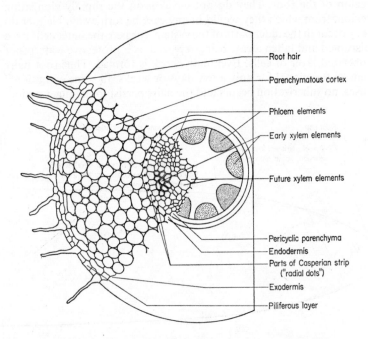

Root hair

Parenchymatous cortex

Phloem elements

Early xylem elements

Future xylem elements

Pericyclic parenchyma

Endodermis

Parts of Casparian strip ("radial dots")

Exodermis

Piliferous layer

FIG. 10. Structure of a dicotyledenous root in the region of maximum water absorption. At a slightly later stage the metaxylem matures, so that the blocks of xylem shown above extend and meet in the centre, giving a four-armed (tetrarch) structure with an area of phloem between each 'arm'. The phloem, since it develops in advance of the xylem, is in a more mature state.

major part is occupied by a large-celled parenchymatous **cortex**, which usually includes many intercellular air spaces. The outer layers of the cortex sometimes consist of smaller, more closely-packed cells, which may later become suberized. This is the **exodermis**. Internal to the cortex lies the **endodermis**, which is a single layer of vertically elongated cells, which appear elliptical or slightly angular in transverse section, their tangential walls being somewhat longer than the radial ones. The protoplast is typically parenchymatous. Part of the cell wall is impregnated with ligno-suberin, in a distinctive pattern. Completely encircling each cell, in the radial and transverse walls, runs a strip of such material called the **Casparian strip** (Fig. 11a). This takes up lignin-specific stains readily. Often, as well as being chemically modified in this way the wall is actually considerably thicker in this region. At a later stage in development, the Casparian strip is greatly augmented so as to involve the whole of the radial walls, and also the inner tangential one (Fig. 11b). In monocotyledons, this additional thickening takes place at a very much earlier stage than in dicotyledons. The significance of these ligno-suberized regions is that they are impermeable, so that any water or solutes passing between the cortex and stele cannot travel within the substance of the radial endodermal walls, but must enter the protoplasts. Although solutes cannot diffuse

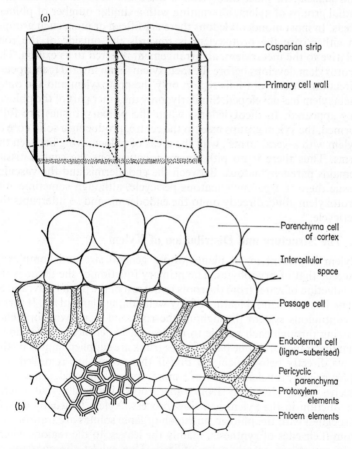

(a)

Casparian strip

Primary cell wall

Parenchyma cell of cortex

Intercellular space

Passage cell

Endodermal cell (ligno–suberised)

Pericyclic parenchyma

Protoxylem elements

Phloem elements

(b)

FIG. 11. Endodermis (a) A diagram of two endodermal cells of the dicotyledonous root. (b) A drawing of part of a transverse section of a monocotyledonous root, as seen under high power of the microscope.

readily through the differentially permeable protoplast, they might otherwise leak from the stele into the cortex within the cellulose framework of the walls, were it not for the ligno-suberization. Loss of solutes from the stele is therefore prevented. In the case of the more extensively modified endodermis referred to above, not even water can penetrate, since here the inner tangential walls are involved. To overcome this difficulty, certain endodermal cells near to each area of protoxylem remain relatively unthickened. These are aptly called **passage cells**.

Within the endodermis, usually on alternate radii, lie the **xylem** and **phloem**. In most dicotyledons there are between two and five radial groups of xylem, alternating with a similar number of phloem areas. In most monocotyledons there are fifteen or more such groups. In either case the protoxylem is towards the outside of the root relative to the metaxylem, an arrangement referred to as exarch. The protoxylem develops before the metaxylem, in an inward (centripetal) direction. In the root hair region only the protoxylem and the outer metaxylem has developed. Similarly, only the outer part of the phloem has appeared. In dicotyledons, when the primary tissues are fully formed, the xylem groups meet in the centre, producing a solid core of xylem with several 'arms', with the areas of phloem lying between the arms. Thus there is no pith. In monocotyledons the central tissue remains parenchymatous. Between the endodermis and the vascular tissue there is a parenchymatous pericycle, although sometimes the protoxylem abuts directly on to the endodermis and so interrupts the pericycle.

2. The Structure and Distribution of Xylem

Xylem is present in all plants whose general size and complexity exceeds that of bryophytes. The primary function of the tissue is the conduction of water from the roots to the rest of the plant body, and as such, it is an essential feature of any well-adapted land plant. It forms a continuous system throughout the root and stem, with branches passing through each petiole to the leaves. Experiments have shown that the branches on one part of a tree trunk are supplied mainly by the roots directly below them, so that if these roots are removed, the appropriate branches above are most severely affected. They only receive water sluggishly from other roots, indicating that lateral conduction in the xylem is a slow process. Xylem is usually closely associated with the phloem, in which organic solutes are transported from their sites of synthesis, mainly the leaves, to the regions where they are stored or otherwise utilized. Thus whilst the contents of xylem move predominantly upwards, those of the phloem travel predominantly, though again not exclusively, downwards.

Detailed descriptions of the various patterns of xylem distribution in stems, roots and leaves would be out of place here, and in any case such information is readily available from any of the well-known text books. Whatever its distribution, xylem is always composed of up to four fundamental cell types. It is the detailed structure of these in relation to their functions with which this section is concerned. Before passing on to a discussion of these basic cell types, however, the distribution of tissues as commonly met with in woody stems will be described.

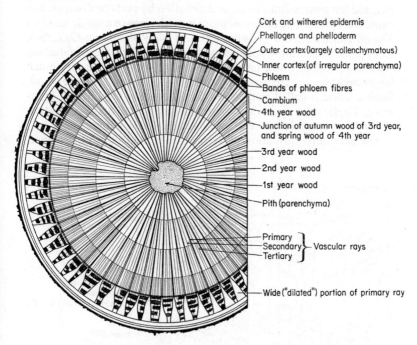

Cork and withered epidermis
Phellogen and phelloderm
Outer cortex (largely collenchymatous)
Inner cortex (of irregular parenchyma)
Phloem
Bands of phloem fibres
Cambium
4th year wood
Junction of autumn wood of 3rd year, and spring wood of 4th year

3rd year wood

2nd year wood

1st year wood

Pith (parenchyma)

Primary ⎫
Secondary ⎬ Vascular rays
Tertiary ⎭

Wide ("dilated") portion of primary ray

FIG. 12. Diagram to show distribution of the principal tissues in the stem of *Tilia*, in its fourth year. *Tilia* is exceptional in the fact that since the phloem is strengthened by fibres, it resists crushing and so forms an unusually wide band at this stage.

The internal structure of most woody Angiosperm stems is similar to that shown in Fig. 12 for *Tilia*. The bulk of the stem is composed of **secondary xylem**, produced as a result of the seasonal activity of the vascular cambium. The detailed cell structure of the secondary xylem of the same plant is shown in Fig. 13. With the onset of each winter, cambial activity ceases, and is resumed the following spring. The xylem formed early in each year consists of wider, less heavily lignified cell types than that produced later. This satisfies the need of the expanding young foliage for copious supplies of water early in the season, and it means that the density of the wood gradually increases as the season progresses. The transition from the very dense wood produced at the end of a season to the first formed tissue of the next season is very abrupt, and its effects are visible to the naked eye. It gives to the wood the appearance of concentric rings called **growth rings**, when seen in transverse section. (The term 'growth rings' is preferable to 'annual rings', for an abrupt change in conditions, such as a sudden temperature shift, or defoliation by pests or diseases, can cause the appearance of two or more growth rings in a single season.) The differentiation into growth rings is, in many plants (e.g. Oak, Ash, Elm) made increasingly obvious by the fact that the water-conducting channels (vessels) which under a lens look like pores, are very much larger and/or more frequent in the early wood than in the late wood. Such a wood is called **ring porous**. In other cases (e.g. Beech, Sycamore, Poplar) the vessels are more uniform in size and distribution throughout a season's growth, producing a **diffuse porous** wood.

The continued formation of xylem causes the stem to increase in

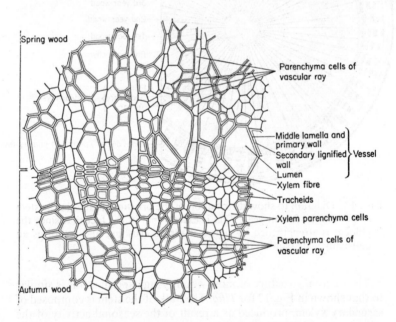

Fig. 13. Drawing of a portion of the secondary xylem of *Tilia*, at the junction of Spring and Autumn wood, and showing three vascular rays. (Note the larger size of the elements in the Spring wood. Since there is much parenchyma and since the other elements are large, the wood is relatively soft.)

girth. Although secondary phloem is produced to the outside of the cambium, it is composed chiefly of thin-walled elements, so that its outer, older cells become crushed. Thus phloem contributes little to increases in stem girth. The oldest vascular tissues (those present in the original unthickened stem) are the small areas of primary xylem and phloem, situated on the inside of the xylem and the outside of the main phloem areas respectively, but the primary phloem does not remain recognizable for long after the commencement of secondary thickening. It should be realized that considerable secondary growth often occurs even during the first year, so that the first year wood consists of both primary and secondary xylem. As in the case of roots (see p. 42) the primary wood is divisible into protoxylem (laid down at a very early stage behind the apical meristem of the shoot) and metaxylem (whose formation commences after the completion of cell elongation). Here, however, the protoxylem is towards the inside relative to the metaxylem, an arrangement known as endarch. The outermost layer in the mature woody stem is a corky periderm. This, by reason of its hard and impervious character, protects the inner tissues from infection, desiccation and mechanical injury. The periderm and phloem together constitute the bark. The centre of the stem is usually occupied by a little parenchymatous pith.

Running in a radial direction, and so crossing the growth rings at right angles, very narrow bands of tissue, often lighter in colour than the wood itself, are visible to the naked eye. These are the **vascular rays**. In transverse section, under high magnification, the rays are seen to consist of rows, one or two cells wide, of roughly rectangular parenchyma cells. In radial longitudinal section the cells again appear rectangular, and are seen to be arranged similarly to the bricks in a wall. In this section, the plane of the 'wall' is viewed at right angles, and the height of the ray is usually seen to be about twelve cells. In tangential longitudinal section the vertical extent of the rays is again visible, but here the cells are practically isodiametric in section for here we are viewing the 'wall', and its 'bricks' end-on.

Some of the rays traverse the entire width of the xylem and phloem, separating it into large blocks, which correspond to the original vascular bundles of the young stem. These are primary rays, and they extend much further vertically than do the other rays. Each year after commencement of secondary growth, some of the cambium cells begin to give rise to parenchyma instead of vascular tissue. The radial files of cells so produced constitute the secondary rays, tertiary rays, and so on, according to the year in which their formation commenced. Each ray will, of course, extend into the vascular tissue of its own year, so that those whose production began most recently will be much shorter when viewed in transverse section than those produced early in the life of the plant.

Although the contents of ray cells are typically parenchymatous, their walls often undergo quite extensive thickening with cellulose, or even a small amount of lignin. In such cases, numerous simple pits and plasmodesmata are prominent, facilitating conduction. Often, numerous starch grains or oil droplets are present, the rays acting as useful storage regions. Probably their primary function, however, is to form an intercommunicating system between the living elements of all the vascular tissues, so that water, with dissolved respiratory gases and mineral salts, as well as other solutes, can be conducted between them. At some point along its length each xylem and phloem element probably contacts at least one ray.

In many trees, the central part of the wood takes on quite a different character from the younger, outer region, often appearing darker in colour. This is because the older xylem, called the **heartwood**, has ceased its water-transporting function, and many of its conducting elements have become occluded, often by ingrowths from adjacent parenchyma cells known as **tyloses**. The elements may also contain air, together with certain organic substances, notably tannins, resins and gums, which are often metabolic waste products. Some of these compounds have antiseptic properties, and it is because of this that commercial timbers such as teak show great resistance to fungal and other harmful attacks. Deposits of this type also impart the characteristic colorations to such timbers as ebony, walnut, and mahogany. The heartwood of such trees as beech and poplar remains light in colour. Sometimes, as in willows, antiseptic substances are lacking in the heartwood, which decays to produce a hollow trunk. The outer wood, which is still functional for conduction, is called **sapwood**. The relative extents of heartwood and sapwood vary greatly in different plants and with the degree of activity which they show. Generally, young or strongly growing parts tend to have a smaller proportion of heartwood than old or slow-growing regions.

As was mentioned earlier, the xylem of Angiosperms is made up of four types of cellular elements (see Fig. 13), each of which makes a definite contribution to the functions of the tissue as a whole. The conduction of water is carried out by **tracheids** and **vessels**. Valuable mechanical support is provided by **fibres**, and **xylem parenchyma**, in conjunction with the vascular rays, forms a living system which permeates the whole vascular tissue, serving for storage of metabolites, and lateral conduction of water. Each is now considered separately.

(a) **Tracheids**. These were the first lignified water-conducting elements to evolve as plant life progressed from aquatic media to colonize the land. In the less highly evolved land plants they fulfilled the dual role of conduction and support. Later evolution has separated these two factors, so that in more advanced forms vessels carry out conduction and fibres function for support, whilst the tracheids from which they both evolved have become less widespread. Thus whilst tracheids are the only lignified xylem elements in pteridophytes and gymnosperms, they are entirely absent from the wood of some angiosperms.

The mature tracheid is a needle-like single cell, ranging up to about 5,000μ in length, and 30μ in diameter (Figs. 14 and 16). Those of the secondary wood are more elongated than those of the primary body.

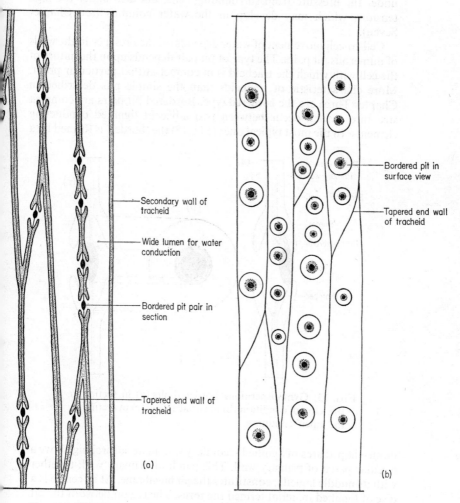

Secondary wall of tracheid

Wide lumen for water conduction

Bordered pit pair in section

Tapered end wall of tracheid

Bordered pit in surface view

Tapered end wall of tracheid

(a)

(b)

FIG. 14. Gymnosperm tracheids (a) in section (b) in surface view.

Towards each end of the cell, one radial wall tapers towards the opposite one, giving it a chisel-like form. Tracheids usually occur in extensive groups, and since their cells overlap and interlock, particularly over the tapered portions, they may together form long strands throughout the plant. In transverse section, tracheids are usually sharply angular. They have lignified secondary walls, but in order to facilitate conduction there is a large lumen. They are dead cells, so that no protoplast hinders the passage of water through them. Lignification is necessary to prevent collapse of the tracheids not only under the pressure from surrounding cells, but also under the high tensions which may develop in the water columns (see Chapter Seven).

Cell-to-cell movement of water depends on the presence in the walls of numerous pit pairs. The type of pit pair depends upon the nature of the cell with which the tracheid is in contact at that particular point. More characteristic of tracheids than the simple pits described in Chapter Three are the **bordered** type. Bordered pit pairs are complex structures which occur between two adjacent lignified conducting elements. In the most typical ones (Fig. 15) the 'border' is formed by a

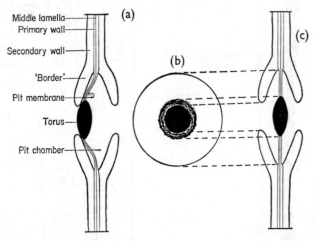

FIG. 15. Gymnospermous bordered pits (a) in section in the 'closed' condition (b) in surface view (c) in section in the 'open' condition.

dome-shaped area of lignified secondary wall material arching above a circular patch of primary wall. This patch of primary wall, together with its middle lamella, constitutes the **pit membrane**. At its centre is a disc of lignified material termed the **torus**. The region between the pit membrane and the border is called the **pit chamber**. The border is

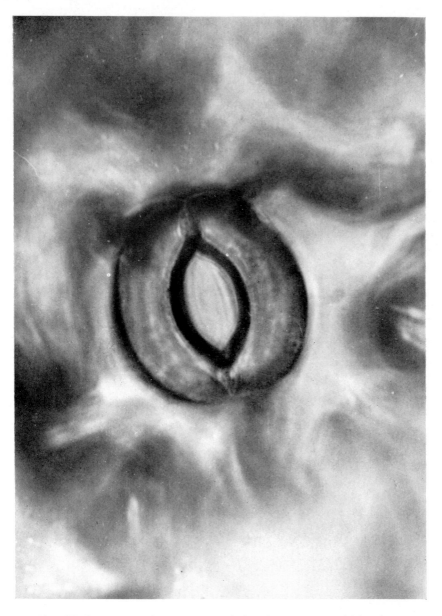

Plate III. Open stoma of *Rumex acetosa* induced to open very widely (about $22\mu \times 11\mu$) on the intact leaf, by enclosing part of the leaf so that the CO_2 content of the air became lowered by photosynthesis. The faint lines visible within the aperture represent the membranous rim of cuticle (see Fig. 21). The dark border is due to the light being reflected away by the sloping ventral walls of the guard cells. (*Photo by* Professor O. V. S. Heath.)

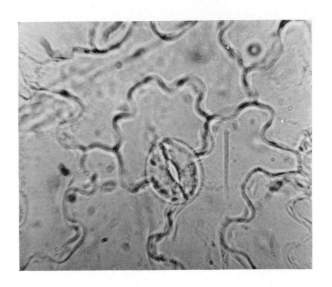

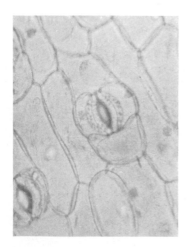
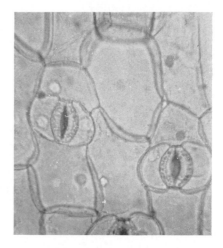

Plate IV. (*a*) Open stoma on the lower epidermal strip of *Fuchsia*; (*b*) and (*c*) Open and closed stomata on lower epidermal strips of *Tradescantia paludosa*. The overlap of the guard cells by the subsidiary cells can be seen, as well as the chloroplasts in the guard cells.

perforated at its apex by a circular pit aperture, somewhat smaller in diameter than the torus. Normally (Fig. 15(c)) the torus lies about midway between the two pit apertures, so that water can pass freely between the two adjacent elements, but under certain circumstances the pit may become aspirated, with the torus displaced to one side so as to block one of the pit apertures (Fig. 15 (a)). This occurs when air enters damaged or dried-out elements. When this happens, because of the close adhesion between water and the pit membrane, the torus is pulled so as to close the aperture on the side still containing an intact water column. In this way, air is prevented from spreading to other elements and forming an extensive air lock in them. Since the xylem contents are often under very high tensions, even a small amount of air could otherwise soon spread to affect many elements.

It has been shown that in the case of at least some gymnosperms definite perforations occur in the pit membrane, which, although they are minute (up to 0.3μ in diameter), may be so numerous as to form what is virtually a network from which the torus is suspended. In such cases it is obvious that less resistance is offered to the movement of water than if the membrane were entire.

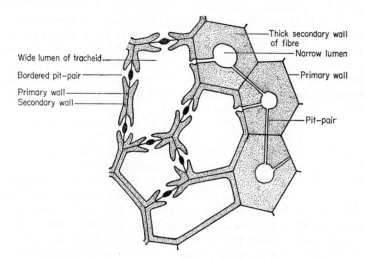

Fig. 16. Gymnospermous tracheids and fibres in transverse section.

Simple pits may occur in lignified conducting elements where they contact cells of the xylem parenchyma or ray parenchyma. Here, there is no torus or border. The secondary wall either ends abruptly at the pit, or tapers towards it, giving a cylindrical or funnel-shaped pit cavity respectively. The pit membrane is again formed by the middle

c

lamella and two thin layers of primary wall. Frequently, a pit pair is bordered on the side of the lignified element, and simple on the side of the parenchyma cell. These are called half-bordered pit pairs, and the torus is reduced or absent in such cases.

(b) Vessels. These occur only in the xylem of angiosperms, apart from one or two very exceptional genera of the gymnosperms. Vessels differ from tracheids in several important respects which render them more conspicuously adapted for the specific purpose of water conduction. Instead of being elongated single cells, they are derived from vertical files of wide, drum-shaped cells, whose transverse walls have become perforated during development to produce long, wide, continuous tubes. Sometimes the entire transverse walls disappear, but often, parts remain, and are called perforation rims or bars. These often run obliquely in longitudinal section, due to the oblique orientation of the transverse walls of the young vessel cells during development. Precise information is lacking as regards the length of vessels, but some are probably many feet long. In trees with ring porous wood, some vessels may extend for the entire length of the plant, and probably only the current year's wood is functional for conduction. In the diffuse porous type the vessels are thought to be shorter, and it seems that several of the most recently formed growth rings are usually in an active conducting state. Most vessels are wider than tracheids, the average diameter being of the order of 250µ. As in the case of tracheids, they bear numerous bordered or simple pits, depending upon the type of cell with which they are in contact. Various types of vessels are illustrated in Fig. 17.

It was pointed out at the beginning of this chapter that the protoxylem, laid down in the early stages of root and shoot development, is much more extensible than the later-formed wood. This results partly from the fact that the fibres are absent from protoxylem, but is also due to the less heavy lignification of the tracheids and vessels. Instead of the whole of the wall, apart from pits, being lignified, the thickening of the protoxylem elements is laid down in two characteristic patterns. In the earliest protoxylem it is in the form of rings or hoops, which suffice to prevent the vessel or tracheid from collapsing for a time, but do not hinder their elongation with the rest of the stem or root, since the rings merely separate from one another. As development proceeds, the elements are laid down with the hoops closer together, and eventually the thickening takes the form of a helix. Whilst this imparts more strength it does not unduly hinder elongation, since when this occurs, the pitch of the helix widens, in a similar way to the stretching of a steel spring. Elements with rings or hoops of thickening are termed **annular** vessels or tracheids (Fig. 17a). Those with helical thickenings are termed **spiral** elements (Fig. 17b).

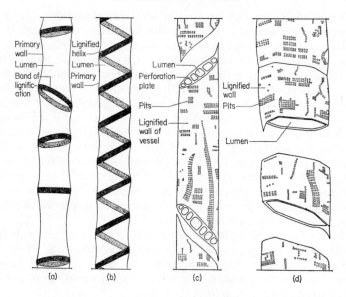

FIG. 17. Vessels, (a) with annular thickening, (b) spiral thickening, (c) narrow pitted vessels with perforation plates, (d) vessels of a highly evolved type (i.e. wide, with no perforation plates).

In the metaxylem, which is the part of the primary xylem laid down after elongation has practically ceased, the pitch of the helical thickening is very close. Successively formed metaxylem elements are progressively more heavily lignified, until finally they reach the stage known as **pitted** vessels and tracheids (Fig. 17c and d) where the only unthickened areas that remain are the pit membranes. It should be noted that once an element has been formed, it does not change to become another type. Thus, for example, the annular and spiral tracheids and vessels remain thickened in the original manner for so long as they are recognizable. In stems they actually become stretched and laterally compressed to such an extent that they disappear before the stem is mature. In the case of roots they persist longer, since they are here subjected to fewer stresses.

(c) **Fibres.** These have been derived from tracheids by greatly increased lignification, so that the lumina of the cells may become completely occluded. All graduations between this extreme type of lignification and that found in tracheids are encountered, these intermediate forms being appropriately termed fibro-tracheids. Fibres resemble tracheids in being angular in transverse section (Fig.

16) and elongated and tapering in longitudinal section. Also like tracheids they interlock vertically, thus facilitating the formation of extensive strands of great strength, though of little elasticity. The heavy lignification of fibres leads to striking modification of the bordered pits. Often, in the thickest-walled fibres, the border becomes incorporated into the thickness of the wall, and is no longer recognizable, so that the pits come to resemble the simple type. Another common occurrence is for the pit aperture to become a narrow slit instead of circular. When this happens on both sides of a pit pair, the slits of the two apertures run in different directions, so that in face view, the pit pair appears X-shaped. Where a fibre contacts a vessel or tracheid, the pit pair is usually bordered on the side of the conducting element, and in the reduced bordered form on the fibre side. Where it contacts a parenchyma cell it is simple on the side of that cell, the fibre side again showing the reduced bordered form.

Fibres vary considerably in their occurrence, not only with the species but with its age and the environmental conditions. They are absent from protoxylem, often present in metaxylem, and nearly always present in secondary xylem, where the autumn wood usually has a larger number than the early wood.

(d) **Xylem parenchyma.** In cell structure, xylem parenchyma resembles ray parenchyma, but here the long axis of each cell runs longitudinally instead of radially. In transverse section, therefore, the cells are practically isodiametric, and, in the secondary wood, commonly appear isolated and scattered throughout the tissue, sometimes more frequently in the spring wood. In the primary xylem they constitute a larger proportion of the tissue, and in protoxylem they may form the largest category of cell types. In longitudinal section they are seen to be elongated, occurring either singly or in short vertical files. As with ray parenchyma, they often become thick-walled, with prominent pitting. Although they remain alive whilst the xylem is in an actively conducting condition, their walls may be lignified at an early stage. Their functions are similar to those of ray parenchyma cells, with which they form an intercommunicating system. At one time, parenchyma cells were thought by some to be essential for the vertical conduction of liquid within vessels and tracheids. This idea has now been almost completely abandoned (see p. 101).

3. The Structure of the Leaf

Leaves are morphologically and anatomically very highly specialized for carrying out the all-important process of photosynthesis. The most obvious part of a typical leaf is the thin, flat blade or **lamina**, which exposes a large relative surface area to the light. The lamina is usually supported by a definite **petiole**, through which its vascular tissues are continuous with those of the stem.

A system of vascular strands permeates the lamina, the largest of which are readily visible to the naked eye as veins. In dicotyledons, the pattern of venation is of the **reticulate** or netted type (see Plate IIb). Here, there is a single main vein, diverging from the vascular system of the stem, and running the length of the leaf. Arising from this, numerous smaller veins appear, passing laterally into the lamina. The larger veins are surrounded by a sheath of tissue which rises conspicuously above the general leaf surface, particularly on the abaxial side, so as to form ribs. The largest of these, which corresponds to the position of the main vein, is the **midrib**. Each vein branches repeatedly into smaller units, and enclosed between the ultimate, often spur-like, branches of the system are very small areas of chlorenchymatous tissue known as **vein islets**. These units are of fairly uniform size, and each photosynthetic cell is near to at least one of the finest vascular strands. In monocotyledons the leaves are phyllodic in origin, that is, they have evolved from petioles which have lost their laminas and become much flattened and chlorenchymatous. Instead of one main vein there are several prominent ones running the entire length of the organ. To the naked eye, this **parallel venation** has quite a different appearance from the reticulate dicotyledonous type. At the microscopic level, however, a system of extremely fine side-branches is produced into the photosynthetic tissue in a similar way to dicotyledons.

The photosynthetic tissue, the **mesophyll**, is enclosed by a protective **epidermis** (Fig. 18) whose structure is considered later. In most cases, the mesophyll is clearly differentiated into two regions, known as the **palisade layer**, and the **spongy layer**. The palisade layer consists of one or two layers of cylindrical cells, just beneath the abaxial epidermis, whose long axes are perpendicular to the plane of the leaf. The cells are thin-walled, with large vacuoles, and a richly chloroplastic cytoplasmic lining. They are in contact to only a limited extent, so that a very extensive air-space system exists, so facilitating gaseous interchange between the cells and their surroundings. The spongy mesophyll lies between the palisade layer and the lower epidermis. The cells are irregularly shaped, and commonly have fewer chloroplasts than those of the palisade layer. They often have a number of radiating arms, the blunt ends of which contact similar regions of adjoining cells. As a result of this irregular arrangement, the air-space system is even more extensive than in the palisade layer. In the case of the *Fuchsia* leaf illustrated in Fig. 18, however, these cells are more regular than in the most typical cases. In total, the internal atmosphere usually represents about one-third of the total leaf volume, though in certain cases the figure may be as little as 10 per cent, or as high as 70 per cent in different kinds of plants. Also, the anatomy of the leaf of any one plant frequently varies according to whether it has developed in bright sunlight or in shaded conditions. The 'shade leaves' of Maple and Beech, for example, possess less palisade tissue, and consequently a more extensive internal atmosphere than the 'sun leaves'.

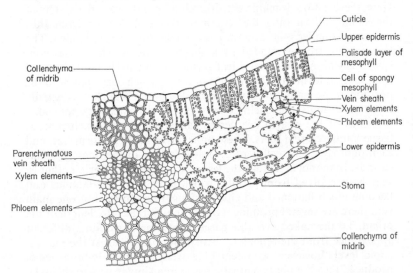

Cuticle

Upper epidermis

Palisade layer of mesophyll

Collenchyma of midrib

Cell of spongy mesophyll

Vein sheath

Xylem elements

Phloem elements

Lower epidermis

Parenchymatous vein sheath

Xylem elements

Phloem elements

Stoma

Collenchyma of midrib

FIG. 18. Vertical section of part of *Fuchsia* leaf, through the midrib region.

The rib tissue which surrounds the larger veins is quite different in character from the mesophyll. It frequently lacks chloroplasts and often, as in the petiole, there is a good deal of collenchyma above and below to provide support without undue loss of flexibility. As the fine branches of the vascular network are approached, the rib tissue peters out, and the number of xylem and phloem elements is progressively reduced, until finally only a single element of each remains. Frequently the phloem disappears before the last xylem element. At these 'bundle ends' the xylem is usually represented by a single file of shortened tracheids, often with spiral thickening. The phloem reduces to a single row of sieve tubes and companion cells, and finally to undifferentiated parenchyma. Although the rib tissue itself has long since disappeared, at no time do the fine vascular traces come into direct contact with either mesophyll cells or air spaces, for they are always jacketed by a bundle sheath, which consists of a tubular layer of closely-fitting parenchyma cells, usually without chloroplasts, and elongated in the direction of the veinlet. Any substances passing to or from the vascular elements must cross this sheath. Mesophyll cells are often seen to converge upon the bundle sheath; presumably this facilitates conduction between them. Sometimes the sheath shows prominent extensions towards the epidermal regions, which almost certainly conduct water to these regions, from where it passes laterally to supply the outer parts of the mesophyll.

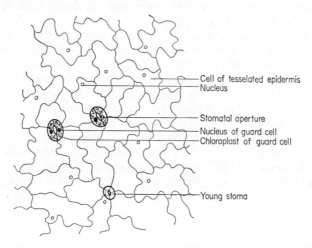

Fig. 19. Drawing of lower epidermis of *Fuchsia* leaf (see also Plate IVa).

The epidermis, as in stems, consists of a single layer of slab-like parenchyma cells. In surface view, the epidermal leaf cells of many dicotyledons are irregular in size and shape, and have a wavy outline, so that adjacent ones closely interlock, in a similar way to the pieces of a jig-saw puzzle (Fig. 19 and Plate IVa). In many monocotyledons the cells are much more regularly arranged, and are elongated parallel to the longitudinal axis of the leaf. The epidermis is of tremendous importance, since not only does it consolidate the entire leaf structure, it also protects the vulnerable inner tissues from desiccation, mechanical injury, and the entry of pathogenic micro-organisms. In order to increase its effectiveness in these respects, a substance known as cutin is produced. Cutin is a waxy material, made up of several types of complex organic compounds, which usually impregnates and stiffens the outermost cell walls. It also forms a quite distinct layer over the surfaces of these walls, called the **cuticle**. The thickness of the cuticle depends upon the species of plant and on the environmental conditions under which it has developed. Its thickness is particularly influenced by the moisture status of the atmosphere, tending to be greatest in plants or parts of plants which have been subjected to conditions of low humidity. A cuticle covers the aerial parts of all land plants, and the development of such an impervious layer to restrict evaporation was a prerequisite for the evolution of a land flora, in the same way as was the development of an efficient water-conducting system. Some plants are structurally adapted for life in habitats where the conditions of water balance are exceptionally unfavourable, and in these the cuticle is more conspicuously developed than in other types of plants (see Chapter Seven).

Just as cutin greatly reduces the loss of water vapour from a plant's surface, so too does it present a barrier to the diffusion of carbon dioxide and oxygen, processes which must take place if the leaf is to carry out its photosynthetic function. This conflicting situation is overcome by a compromise between the needs of photosynthesis on the one hand, and prevention of desiccation on the other. The compromise is effected by the presence of numerous small pores, the **stomata**, in the epidermis, through which exchange of gases may take place between the atmosphere and the air-space system of the leaf. Stomata are clearly of great physiological significance, and are discussed fully in relation to the physiology of the plant in Chapter Five.

CHAPTER FIVE

Transpiration

It is a fact of common observation that water will evaporate into un-saturated air from any moist surface with which it is in contact. The evaporation of water from the surface of plants is called transpiration. The amount of water available to the root systems of land plants is often very limited, so that, as was pointed out in Chapter Four, a truly terrestrial flora could not have evolved were it not for the protection afforded by the cuticle against the hazard of excessive evaporation. This protection cannot, however, be complete, since moist cell surfaces in contact with air must be maintained so that gaseous metabolic raw materials and waste products can pass between the plant and its environment. These gases, carbon dioxide and oxygen, can only be utilized in solution, in which state they travel within the tissues by diffusion.

1. The Sites of Transpiration

The most rapid gaseous exchanges take place in connection with photosynthesis. As will be evident from the discussion in Chapter Four, the extent of moist cell surfaces in contact with air is very considerable in the mesophyll of leaves, and it is therefore not sur-prising that a great deal of evaporation takes place from these organs, chiefly through open stomata. This is called **stomatal transpiration**. Whilst the cuticle affords indispensable protection from evaporation, it is not entirely impermeable to gases, so that some **cuticular tran-spiration** is inevitable over the entire aerial surface of the plant. The cuticle has often been observed to be minutely but deeply fissured, particularly as it ages, a feature which probably increases its perme-ability. On the other hand, in many plants the cuticle may become impregnated with additional waxy or resinous substances which tend to increase its effectiveness. In the case of woody plants, cork is present as a protective layer, and this is generally less permeable than even the cuticle. Here, however, lenticels are present. These are areas of loosely-packed tissue which open to the surface and appear as small raised dots, on the bark of twigs, and on certain other organs, such as potato tubers. Their function is to allow respiratory gases to penetrate to the internal living tissue. Again, water will inevitably be lost, this time by **lenticular transpiration**.

The three sites of transpiration outlined above are by no means of

61

equal importance, and lenticular transpiration in particular is of little significance. This fact is borne out by the observation that undamaged potato tubers lose weight very slowly indeed during storage, so that the presence of abundant lenticles in the corky outer layer does little to decrease the effectiveness of that layer with regard to water conservation.

Careful measurements on species with hypostomal leaves (those with stomata on the lower surface only) clearly indicate that the transpiration rate from the lower surface greatly exceeds that from the upper surface when the stomata are open. In some cases, this is partly because the lower surface bears a thinner cuticle, and so has a slightly higher rate of cuticular transpiration, but there is no doubt whatever that the principal reason for such results is that stomatal transpiration greatly exceeds the cuticular component. In the special cases of young leaves, or shade leaves, the cuticle may be very thin, so that here cuticular transpiration accounts for a larger proportion of the total. In general, however, the cuticular loss of water from a plant with open stomata represents less than 10 per cent of the total transpiration, although there are naturally wide variations between the relative rates in different leaves. When stomata close, the total measured transpiration rate drops to a small fraction of that observed when the stomata are reasonably wide open.

2. Stomata

In view of the great importance of stomatal transpiration, it is desirable to consider the distribution, structure and physiology of stomata in some detail.

(a) **Distribution.** Since the function of stomata is to facilitate gaseous exchange, they are to be found on any chlorenchymatous organ, but are present in particularly large numbers on leaves. Their frequency varies markedly with the species of plant, and the environmental conditions, the chief factor here being the humidity of the atmosphere. Generally, the drier the situation, the greater the number of stomata per unit area (p. 106). They are usually more abundant on the abaxial (lower) leaf surface, where well over one hundred per square millimetre are frequently present. Often they are entirely absent from the adaxial surface, especially in the case of broad-leaved trees. In one investigation on the sunflower, approximately 85 stomata per sq. mm were found on the adaxial surface, and 156 per sq. mm on the abaxial side.[1] Stomata occur also on herbaceous stems and, in a reduced form, on floral organs. Hydrophytes are characterized by having few, or rather degenerate, stomata on submerged parts. Here

[1] Data of Eckerson, Bot. Gaz., **46** (1908).

they serve no function, but their presence indicates the terrestrial ancestry of these plants.

(b) **Structure.** Stomata consist essentially of a pair of specialized epidermal cells, the **guard cells**, surrounding an elliptical **stomatal aperture**. The apertures are of the order of only a few microns in length and breadth; in the sunflower, for example, the maximum dimensions have been given as $22\mu \times 8\mu$.[1] In most cases the guard cells are slightly depressed below the general level of the epidermis, whilst in some plants they are even confined to deep pits or grooves. This marked depression of stomata is of considerable ecological significance, being associated with the xerophytic habit (see p. 126 and Figs. 32, 33, 34).

Guard cells differ from ordinary epidermal cells in several important respects (see Figs. 19, 20, 21 and Plates III and IV). Most are

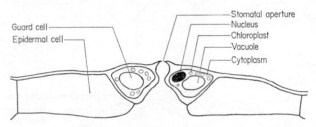

Guard cell
Epidermal cell
Stomatal aperture
Nucleus
Chloroplast
Vacuole
Cytoplasm

FIG. 20. Drawing of a median vertical section through a stoma of *Fuchsia* (contents of epidermal cells not shown).

approximately kidney-shaped in surface view. Unlike the epidermal cells, they contain pale chloroplasts. They also have more prominent nuclei, and a greater proportion of cytoplasm. The walls of guard cells are heavily and asymetrically thickened with cutinized cellulose. The pattern of distribution of this additional wall material varies widely between different plants. This material does, however, play an essential part in bringing about changes in shape of the guard cells, which in turn control the size of the aperture. One common situation is that shown for *Pelargonium zonale* in Fig. 21.

Guard cells contain a considerable amount of carbohydrate, sometimes predominantly in the form of prominent starch grains, and at other periods mainly as dissolved sugars, although the total carbohydrate content probably varies little. Most such material originates from other green cells, and not from the feeble photosynthetic activity of the guard cell chloroplasts. Externally, guard cells are covered by a cuticle.

The epidermal cells immediately adjacent to the guard cells are called **subsidiary cells**. Sometimes these are identical with the rest of the epidermal cells, but in many cases they are quite different in shape and/or structure (see Plate III). Especially in this latter case, subsidiary cells play an important part in the functioning of the stoma.

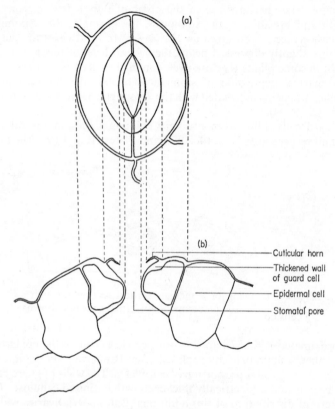

(a)

(b)

Cuticular horn

Thickened wall of guard cell

Epidermal cell

Stomatal pore

FIG. 21. Stoma of *Pelargonium zonale*[1] (a) in surface view and (b) in median section.

(c) Physiology of Stomata.

(i) *Diffusion through stomatal apertures*. It has already been pointed out that the walls of leaf mesophyll cells are normally impregnated with water. This is due both to the imbibitional capacity of cellulose, and to capillarity as a result of the presence of fine spaces between the cellulose units. As water evaporates from these walls, the intercellular air becomes more saturated with water vapour, and this increasing concentration of water molecules means that diffusion

[1] Redrawn from Heath, Ann. Bot. N.S.5,. (1941).

takes place through the stomata into the external air. The rate at which diffusion proceeds depends largely upon the steepness of the diffusion pressure gradient, that is, the rate at which the water vapour concentration changes with distance over the diffusion path. At the cell surfaces, the air will normally be nearly fully saturated, having a D.P.D. approaching zero. Since the length of the diffusion path to the stomata is constant, the diffusion pressure gradient, and hence the rate of transpiration, depends upon the D.P.D., or humidity, of the air just above the stomata.

With completely motionless external air, it is possible to visualize the formation, above each stoma, of a gradually extending dome-shaped mass of water vapour, due to the spreading out of the water molecules as they emerge from the apertures at widely different angles. The concentration of water vapour across each diffusion shell from a high level just above each stoma, to about the same level as the surrounding atmosphere at its circumference. As the shells build up and increase in thickness, so the diffusion pressure gradient of water vapour from the stomata to the main mass of external air decreases in steepness, and the rate of transpiration falls. If the leaf is swept by air currents, however, the shells cannot form, there is no accumulation of saturated air, and so the diffusion pressure gradient is steep. Thus moving air favours a much higher rate of transpiration than still air, all other conditions being equal.

Since leaves are, first and foremost, photosynthetic structures, it is important that the photosynthetic activity of a given region of leaf tissue should be at as high a level as the prevailing external conditions will allow. It is desirable, for example, that the rate should not at any time be limited by the rate at which carbon dioxide can diffuse into the leaf. However, since usually less than 1 per cent of the surface area of a leaf is composed of stomatal apertures, even when they are fully open, it would at first sight appear extremely likely that inward diffusion of carbon dioxide would take place too slowly to allow a high photosynthetic rate, particularly since the concentration of this gas in ordinary air is only about 0.03 per cent. In spite of this, it has been shown conclusively that when stomata are open, they are capable of admitting all the carbon dioxide which can be utilized in photosynthesis under natural conditions of temperature, light intensity and carbon dioxide concentration. Furthermore, it has been found that in order to account for certain measured photosynthetic rates, carbon dioxide must, in these cases, have diffused through stomata at a rate per unit area of aperture about sixty times faster than that at which the gas can be absorbed by a continuous surface of a strong caustic soda solution.

Whilst stomata provide such an extremely efficient means for the exchange of metabolic gases, the same considerations apply equally well to the loss of water vapour. Thus, when stomata are fully open, water may be lost through them about fifty times faster than from a continuous wet surface of equal area, under equivalent conditions. Also, the rate of transpiration from a given area of leaf is commonly in the region of half the evaporation rate from an equal area of a continuous wet surface, in spite of the fact that stomatal apertures represent perhaps only 1 per cent of the leaf surface area. Another important fact which has been discovered is that stomata only exert an appreciable effect on the transpiration rate when they are within the range between roughly half maximum width and complete closure.

The clue as to why stomata allow such efficient gaseous exchange was provided by important experiments which simulated their mode of operation. Rates of evaporation from water surfaces separated from air of known humidity by thin septa perforated in various ways were measured. Some septa contained single pores of various sizes; others were perforated by many pores of equal sizes but separated by different distances. Largely as a result of such experiments, it has been found possible to explain their efficiency on the basis of the formation of diffusion shells.

Fig. 22a represents a water surface (or a region of completely saturated air) separated from motionless, unsaturated air by an

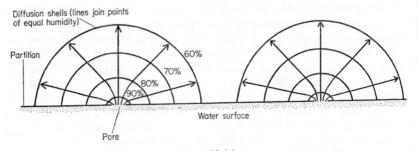

FIG. 22 (a).

impervious septum, in which two small apertures are situated at a considerable distance apart. Diffusion shells build up above each pore as indicated, the rates of diffusion through each being equal. Water molecules escaping at the perimeter of a pore will diffuse away much more rapidly than those which emerge from the central part, because the motion of the latter is impeded by the presence of other water molecules all around them, whereas the former can quickly move outwards, not being equally surrounded by other water molecules.

Consider now the case where the two pores are gradually brought closer together (Fig. 22b). Before long, the two diffusion shells begin

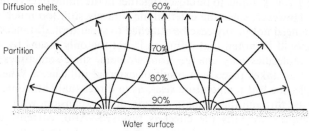

Fig. 22 (b).

to overlap, and in the overlap region the concentration of water vapour will be much greater than in either of the two separate shells, so that the rate of evaporation from the corresponding part of each pore will fall. At the point where the two pores just come into contact, the diffusion shells will nearly coincide, and although the total area of the combined pore is equal to that of the separate pores, the total evaporation rate is very greatly reduced. Another way of stating this is that since the perimeter of the pores is reduced when they join, and since the rate of evaporation from around the perimeter of a pore is greater than that near the centre, the total evaporation rate is reduced.

When these principles are applied to stomata, it becomes easy to see why they allow high rates of gaseous diffusion. Also, the fact that diffusion through these apertures is proportional to their perimeters rather than their areas makes it possible to understand why it is that stomata exert the most effective control over the range of aperture size between roughly half their maximum dimensions and complete closure. Any small aperture has a large perimeter in relation to its area, so that small increases or decreases in area mean relatively large increases or decreases in perimeter diffusion. After a certain pore size has been reached, however, especially in the case of elliptical pores like stomata, relative changes in perimeter are much smaller when the area changes.

When the pores in a multiperforate septum are spaced more than about ten diameters apart, adjoining diffusion shells do not appreciably overlap and interfere with one another in still air, so that the maximum rate of diffusion takes place through each pore. In moving air, the pores can be even closer together without interference taking place. It is interesting to note in this connection that stomata are seldom set less than ten diameters apart, although here the situation is more complicated due to the fact that the apertures are variable. Thus stomata which are ten diameters apart when only partly open may not be so when maximum size is attained. Also it should be remembered that stomata may not be uniformly distributed over the leaf's surface, tending, for example, to be closer together in the immediate vicinity of veins. However, since the external air is rarely still, too much significance need not in any case be attached to separation distances.

It should be noted that diffusion is not the only means by which water molecules may emerge from stomata, since sometimes mass flow of air takes place as a result of external influences. When, for example, the leaf temperature rises, as in direct sunlight, some air is displaced through the stomata as a result of expansion, whilst when the temperature falls the effect is reversed. Also, currents of air moving over a leaf may bring about some mass movement of air by creating suction effects. Finally, some movement of air into and out of leaves via stomata may result from the waving of leaves by wind action. Whenever mass flow of air takes place, transpiration is increased.

(ii) *Control of aperture size.* The size of stomatal apertures is controlled by the relative turgor of the guard cells and the subsidiary cells. When guard cell turgor is relatively low, the pore is closed. As turgor increases as a result of an influx of water from the subsidiary cells, the walls of the guard cells become stretched .The cellulose units making up these walls run approximately at right angles to the long axis of the cells, so that they elongate. The heavily thickened region of the inner border, however, offers great resistance to elongation, and the effect of the greater elongation of the outer wall is to make the guard cells more curved in surface view, pulling the thickened inner walls of neighbouring guard cells away from one another, and widening the pore. The separation is probably aided by the fact that, in many cases, end portions of each guard cell (the parts not surrounding the aperture) are less heavily thickened than the rest, and push against their opposite numbers as turgor increases. This is particularly the case in the stomata of grasses, where the lumen in each guard cell assumes the form of a dumb-bell (Fig. 23). There are many variations on this mechanism, associated with differences in structure or position of the guard cells, but all seem to be actuated by turgor changes.

Evidence that it is the balance in turgor between the guard cells and subsidiary cells which actuates stomatal movements has been obtained by Professor O. V. S. Heath, using both *Cyclamen* and *Tradescantia* as test material. If one guard cell is punctured by a micro-needle and the sap allowed to escape, the cell collapses, and the aperture closes on that side. If, however, a subsidiary cell is punctured in this way, the guard cell on the same side bulges, and the pore opens wider. Also it can be shown that the osmotic potential of guard cells is less than subsidiary cells when the pore is closed, whereas it is much greater when the aperture is wide open. Another useful piece of information

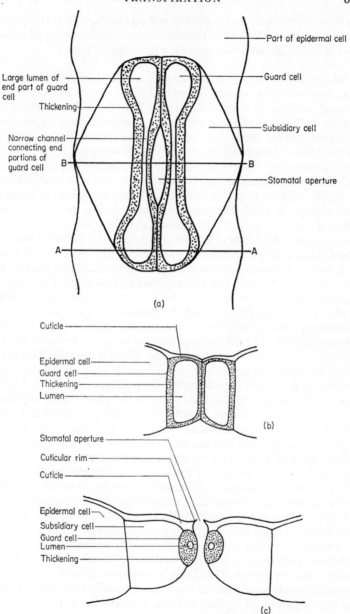

FIG. 23. Structure of 'grass type' stoma (a) Section parallel to leaf surface, (b) Vertical section in plane AA, (c) Vertical section in plane BB (cytoplasmic contents not shown).

in this connection is that in rapidly wilting plants, stomata frequently open more widely for a time. This may be attributed to an initial greater loss of turgor by subsidiary cells than by the guard cells.

(iii) *Factors controlling guard cell movements.* Stomata are extremely sensitive to a wide variety of internal and external influences. The central problem is that of explaining how these factors affect the turgor relationship of guard cells. Since so many factors are involved, it seems at least likely that more than one mechanism must be involved. Most of the problems are still largely unsolved, mainly because of the extremely complicated nature of stomatal responses, which renders the experimental approach to their study exceedingly difficult.

In the majority of plants, there is a diurnal periodicity of stomatal movements, in which the apertures widen during the daytime, and close in the evening. (It should be noted that there are some exceptions to this type of behaviour, particularly amongst the succulent plants of the *Cactaceae* and *Crassulaceae*, in which stomata open only at night, a feature associated with their xerophytic habit. Plants such as the *Hydrangea* and Potato are also atypical.) These diurnal movements are well known to be correlated with changes in the state of carbohydrate in the guard cells. When stomata are open under natural conditions, the carbohydrate is represented chiefly by sugars, and closure is marked by the disappearance of much of the sugars and the conspicuous formation of starch grains. There is little variation in the total carbohydrate content. It appears likely, then, that shifts in the starch $\rightleftharpoons$ sugar balance could control these diurnal movements.[1] When starch changes into sugars, the D.P.D. of the guard cells is increased, and water flows into them from subsidiary cells, raising their turgor. When the sugar content falls, the flow is reversed. These diurnal changes do, in many species, continue for several days even when plants are maintained under constant environmental conditions, but no satisfactory explanation of this behaviour is forthcoming. It is also noteworthy that the onion, *Allium cepa*, contains no starch at all, and it has so far been impossible to demonstrate an endogenous diurnal rhythm in this plant, although the stomata do, of course, respond normally to factors such as light and carbon dioxide.

Diurnal rhythms greatly complicate the experimental study of stomatal behaviour, since they tend to be superimposed upon the effects of other factors. Thus there is sometimes difficulty in knowing whether an observed effect is due to an experimentally varied factor, or to an endogenous rhythm, or to an interaction of both.

---

[1] It should be noted that the state of carbohydrate in guard cells (i.e. a preponderance of starch at night, and of sugar in the daytime) is quite the reverse of that in the leaf as a whole.

The effects of light and CO_2.

Stomata are extremely sensitive to changes in light intensity, closing when darkened, and opening again when illuminated. These responses are often immediate. Light sensitivity has been explained on the basis of the effects brought about on guard cells by changes in carbon dioxide concentration, these changes themselves being the result of changes in light intensity.

In order to simplify and shorten what would otherwise become a very involved discussion, the most widely held theory put forward to explain this sensitivity will be reviewed, together with some of the evidence both in favour of, and against it.

(i) In the light, photosynthesis brings about a gradual reduction in the CO_2 concentration in the internal tissues of the leaf, so that the level of acidity in the contents of the leaf cells, including the guard cells, is lowered.

(ii) Starch in the cytoplasm of guard cells is in equilibrium with glucose monophosphate, the reversible reaction being catalysed by the enzyme starch phosphorylase, and the equilibrium point being pH dependent. The rise in pH brought about by the removal of CO_2 causes the equilibrium to be displaced to the right, the amount of starch decreasing, and the concentration of glucose monophosphate rising.

$$\text{Starch} + H_3PO_4 \overset{\text{starch phosphorylase}}{\rightleftharpoons} \text{Glucose monophosphate}$$

(iii) Since phosphoric acid is used in this process, no increase in osmotic potential takes place until the glucose phosphate is hydrolysed to form glucose, and giving the phosphoric acid back again.

$$\text{Glucose monophosphate} + H_2O \overset{\text{phosphatase}}{\rightleftharpoons} \text{Glucose} + H_3PO_4$$

When this take place, the D.P.D. of the guard cell sap rises, bringing about the influx of water from neighbouring cells and the consequent increase in turgor which causes stomatal opening.

(iv) In darkness, these processes are reversed. Respiratory CO_2 accumulates, the pH falls, starch is re-formed, water flows out of the guard cells, and turgor is lost.

Supporting evidence for this type of mechanism comes from the following data:

(i) As already stated, diurnal variations in carbohydrate equilibria occur, which could be light-dependent. Under natural day-length conditions, stomatal opening is found to be correlated with increases in sugar concentration, osmotic potential and pH, together with reduced starch content. When stomata close, the reverse changes are detectable.

(ii) The presence of starch phosphorylase has been demonstrated in the guard cells of such plants as tobacco and broad bean, and the equilibrium point of the reaction which it catalyses is known to be influenced by pH in a manner consistent with the suggested mechanism.

(iii) Treatments with buffer solutions, as well as exposure to the vapours of acetic acid or ammonia, have shown that increasing the pH of the leaf tissues is often accompanied by a reduction in the starch content of guard cells and by stomatal opening, even in the dark. Decreases in pH have the opposite effects; in some cases closure takes place even in bright light.

(iv) If the external supply of CO_2 is restricted, starch disappears, and stomata open. Stomata are sensitive to small changes in CO_2 concentration, at very low levels. The most sensitive responses are shown over the range from about 0.03 per cent to 0.01 per cent in the light, and 0.01 per cent to zero in the dark. Thus the optimum conditions for stomatal opening are a high light intensity, coupled with a very low concentration of CO_2. If illuminated leaves are sandwiched between two microscope slides, or placed with their laminas in a closed tube, stomata usually widen appreciably as the available CO_2 becomes depleted by photosynthesis. When a free air supply is restored, the stomata revert to their former condition. Similar movements take place if currents of air containing controlled concentrations of CO_2 are passed over plants. In this case, the movements take place even in the dark, though they are less marked.

The amount of CO_2 present in the region which would affect the pH of the guard cell contents is governed by the balance between the prevailing respiratory and photosynthetic intensities of both the guard cells, and the mesophyll as a whole. Since guard cells show little photosynthetic activity as compared with the mesophyll, at normal light intensities the ratio of photosynthesis to respiration is much closer to unity than in mesophyll cells, where it is often of the order of 10:1. Because the most delicate balance exists in the guard cells, it is not surprising that changes in the relative rates of the two processes here are far more effective in controlling guard cell movements than similar changes in the mesophyll as a whole, although the latter do have some effect. Thus, in one series of experiments it was found that if the stomatal surface was illuminated with various wavelengths of light, only $\frac{1}{5}$ to $\frac{1}{18}$ of the intensity was required to produce a given degree of opening than when the guard cells received light passing through the leaf when the astomatal surface was illuminated. This clearly indicates that it is the amount of light which the guard cells receive that is important in bringing about stomatal movements.

Stomatal responses to light and CO_2 cannot be explained solely on the basis of the starch phosphorlyase mechanism put forward on p. 71. There are, for instance, certain plants to which it cannot apply at all, since they lack starch. Examples are the onion, and certain albino forms of cereal plants; in both cases normal stomatal responses occur to changes in light intensity and CO_2 concentration. It is possible that here a polysaccharide other than starch might be involved, such as the fructosans which abound in onion plants, but there is no direct evidence that this is so. Also, there is some experimental support for the idea of a direct light effect on stomata which is completely independent of CO_2. Furthermore, the midday closure of stomata which takes place in certain species (see p. 75) is thought to be attributable to increases in CO_2 concentration, and yet no convincing evidence has been obtained which demonstrates a correlated increase in starch content at that time. The same is true of plants whose stomata have been induced to close by giving a period of darkness at abnormal times of day. It is quite possible, therefore, that light can affect stomata quite independently of the starch ⇌ sugar balance, and that the latter is influenced chiefly by such factors as diurnal rhythms, and the availability of water.

Finally, it should be noted that facts relating to pH values of guard cells must be regarded cautiously. Hydrolysis of starch must presumably take place in the cytoplasm, which would be expected to be reasonably well buffered. It is therefore not easy to see how the small changes in CO_2 concentration which affect stomata could appreciably alter the pH value. It is certainly unlikely that these changes could be caused simply by the CO_2 dissolving in the cytoplasm. It is now envisaged that a non-photosynthetic method of CO_2 assimilation is involved, in which the gas is more or less directly incorporated with an acceptor to form organic acids, such as malic acid. This would be more effective in lowering the pH. Such a process of light—independent CO_2 fixation occurs extensively in the succulent plants of the *Cactaceae* and *Crassulaceae*, and has also been shown to take place in such widely unrelated plants as the onion, tobacco, rhubarb, bean and tulip. It should also be noted that the pH differences that have been observed between the guard cells of open and closed stomata relate to the vacuolar sap, whereas, as stated above, any pH changes affecting starch hydrolysis must take place in the cytoplasm. The extent to which the two may be correlated is not known.

The effects of water deficits

Whenever transpiration rates begin to exceed absorption rates, a water deficit is initiated in the tissues. Slight water deficits occur frequently in most plants, particularly, of course, during periods of low rainfall, and these are often made up by continued absorption when the transpiration rate falls, as at night. When transpiration exceeds absorption over a prolonged period, much more severe water deficits are incurred.

The behaviour of stomata in response to these deficits is complex, and not very uniform, so that few generally valid remarks may be made on the subject. Usually, however, by the time that permanent wilting has set in, stomata will have closed. Stomatal behaviour depends a good deal upon the speed at which a water deficit is incurred. If this is rapid, initial widening frequently takes place. This is due to the fact that subsidiary cells lose turgor before guard cells, because of the resistance offered to the passage of water by the intervening cell wall. In this connection, it is noteworthy that guard cells seem to be more isolated than the rest of the epidermal cells, lacking, for example, plasmodesmata. When a water deficit is quickly made up, by giving a free water supply and exposure to a humid atmosphere, turgor is often regained more quickly by the subsidiary cells, and temporary closure may occur. When, on the other hand, a water deficit builds up only gradually, progressive stomatal closure takes place in many species, because the longer time period allows the guard cells and subsidiary cells to adjust their turgor relationships. Conversely, gradual recovery brings about progressive re-opening of stomata.

It seems likely that stomatal responses to water deficit are at least partly due to changes in the CO_2 concentration in the leaf. It has been shown that when a deficit is incurred, sugar may be rapidly converted into starch in the guard cells, with a consequent loss of turgor, a conversion which appears to be correlated with an increase in the CO_2 level. Such an increase could be brought about by either increased respiration, or decreased photosynthesis, or, most probably, by both. The manner in which these processes are affected by a water deficit is not known. It is again interesting to note (see p. 70) that the changes in starch $\rightleftharpoons$ sugar balance in guard cells in response to a water deficit are the reverse of those taking place in the leaf as a whole, where starch becomes converted into sugar.

The degree of water deficit necessary to bring about closure is very variable. In some cases the response begins at an early stage, but there are some instances where the stomata of even seriously wilted plants have remained open. The stomata of some plants undergo a whole series of opening and closure movements.

Stomatal closure in response to the water factor is of considerable ecological significance. When many types of plants are grown under conditions of unfavourable water balance, their stomata remain closed for a longer period each day than when the same plants are subjected to less exacting conditions. As the deficit increases in severity, so the period of closure extends. Behaviour of this type is particularly characteristic of xerophytes.

The effect of temperature changes

Under most circumstances, increases in air temperature up to about 30° C tend to increase the size of stomatal apertures. Below freezing point, on the other hand, stomata are rarely open, even with a favourable light intensity. In experiments on alfalfa, Loftfield[1] found that over the range from 0° C to 30° C the time required for stomatal opening was halved for each 10 deg C rise in temperature. Thus, for example, opening took place in four hours at 10° C, but the same movement at 30° C took only an hour. Such temperature effects have been attributed to changes in the rate of starch phosphorolysis. Above about 35° C the protoplasm is injured, and closure takes place.

In certain species, such as coffee and onion, another type of temperature response is superimposed upon these effects. Here, stomatal closure occurs for a short period each day around noon. At one time, this midday closure was thought to be in response to a water deficit, but it is not accompanied by the increased starch content normally associated with this condition (see p. 74). It now seems likely that, once again, it is a response to a change in CO_2 concentration. The temperature coefficient for respiration is higher than that for photosynthesis, so that when the temperature rises, the rate of the former increases more than that of the latter, the carbon dioxide level gradually rises, and the stomata close. In the case of onion, the accumulation of carbon dioxide takes place in the hollow cavity of the leaf, which is in poor communication with the outside air.

(d) The significance of stomata in water economy. Water conservation is one of the major problems encountered by all terrestrial organisms. The cuticle of land plants restricts evaporation with considerable success, but a truly continuous layer would be even more effective in guarding against desiccation. However, as was pointed out earlier, the requirement for the exchange of metabolic gases makes such an uninterrupted layer impossible. Unfortunately, cutin does not possess the ideal properties of permeability to metabolic gases, but impermeability to water vapour. If this were the case, however, the necessity for stomata would be obviated. In this connection, it is noteworthy that some experiments in which carbon dioxide 'labelled' with C^{14} has been used indicate that this gas can pass through the cuticle, but the extent to which this occurs is small, and there is no suggestion that the cuticle is any more permeable to CO_2 than to water. As we have seen, stomata allow high rates of gaseous diffusion when open, but by partial or complete closure at certain periods the rate is considerably reduced (see also Section 3(b) p. 82). Stomata are normally completely closed during the hours of darkness, so that unnecessary loss of water is avoided when photosynthesis would not in any case be taking place. It would also be advantageous for stomatal closure to occur at times when severe wilting is imminent. It should be

[1] 'The behaviour of stomata' Carnegie Inst. Wash. Publ. **82**, 1–142 (1908).

realized that small, temporary water deficits occur frequently, and present no hazard to the plant, since they are readily rectified when the transpiration rate falls in the evening. If stomatal closure took place at these times, metabolism would be unnecessarily interrupted. Obviously, there can be no anticipation as to whether a small water deficit is merely temporary, or whether it is the prelude to a prolonged, hazardous water shortage. As we saw in the last section, the degree of water deficit which brings about stomatal closure is extremely variable.

The importance of stomata, then, seems to rest in the fact that closure takes place (a) at night, avoiding unnecessary transpiration, and (b) usually at some stage during a water deficit, so assisting in the recovery of turgor (though sometimes not until after visible wilting has actually taken place).

(e) **Methods of studying the degree of opening of stomata.** Several useful methods exist for obtaining information as to the degree of opening of stomata; only an outline of some of these can be given here. It must be borne in mind throughout that, owing to the extreme sensitivity of stomata to slight changes in conditions, any experimental procedure is itself liable to bring about changes from the stomatal condition just prior to the investigation. Thus the results must be related to the rather artificial conditions under which the experiment is performed. Also, stomata sometimes close in response to the mechanical handling which may be required in setting up an experiment, so that, where possible, a period of a few hours should be allowed for recovery before the investigation is commenced. The student should, as always in experimental work, adopt a critical approach, thinking out for himself the limitations of the method used. In class experiments, the average of the results obtained by the individual students should be recorded where possible.

(i) *Microscopic examination.* The dimensions of actual individual pores may be measured with the aid of a calibrated micrometer eyepiece. In some cases it is perfectly possible to carry out observations upon intact leaves, but, especially where the epidermis is hairy, it is often more convenient to quickly strip off a portion of epidermis, immediately plunging it into absolute alcohol, and later examining it in a drop of this liquid on a slide. This last procedure was advocated by Lloyd, who claimed that fixation is so rapid that the aperture remains unchanged. It does seem likely, though, that some change does occur during the stripping process, if only because of changes in turgor pressure of the cells of the strip when released from the influence of the remaining leaf cells. The chief disadvantages of the technique are that large variations are apt to occur between individual stomata, necessitating the laborious measurement of many stomata, that there is uncertainty as to the exact parts of the curved pore boundaries to measure, and that it is difficult to focus on these curved surfaces at the appropriate level. Furthermore, if living material is being used, the illumination of the specimen may affect the aperture size.

In cases where direct observation is impossible, and where epidermal strips cannot be obtained, another technique is often successful. The surface of the leaf is moistened with a little acetone, and a thin film of cellulose acetate is then applied and held firmly in position. The softened film forms a surface replica of the leaf, and after a few minutes' hardening, it may be peeled away and examined microscopically.

(ii) *Molisch's infiltration method*. The lower the surface tension at the interface of a liquid and a leaf, the smaller is the stomatal aperture which the liquid will penetrate. (Indeed, the fact that rainwater has too high a surface tension to enter even wide-open stomata is of obvious importance in preventing the flooding of the mesophyll and hence the interruption of photosynthesis.)

A series of liquids is prepared in such a way as to give a steady gradation in surface tensions. A drop of each liquid is applied to the test leaf. Penetration is easily detected with the naked eye, since the flooding of the intercellular spaces imparts an obvious darker green appearance to the affected patch of tissue. Suitable liquids are mixtures of such pairs of liquids as n-dodecane/liquid paraffin, or butanol/glycerine. A series of eleven liquids is usual. No. 1 is pure n-dodecane or butanol, which will penetrate slightly open pores, and No. 11 is pure liquid paraffin or glycerine, which will only pass through much wider apertures. Liquids Nos. 2–10 are mixtures, with an increasing proportion of one constituent, and a correspondingly decreasing proportion of the other. From the composition of that liquid whose surface tension is just low enough to penetrate, an indication of the pore size may be gained.

Although less quantitative than Lloyd's procedure, it is possible by this method to rapidly test the effects of changed environmental conditions on stomatal widths. The highest-numbered liquid which penetrates under the different conditions or at different times of day, is recorded, using, of course, different areas of leaf for each application. The method is extremely simple, and can be used in the field, on intact plants. It is impossible, however, to allow for variations between individual stomata.

(iii) *Stahl's cobalt chloride method*. Pieces of absorbent paper, previously soaked in a 3 per cent solution of cobalt chloride, are blue when perfectly dry, and are hygroscopic, the colour changing to pink when they are allowed to absorb water. Small strips or squares of the dry paper are quickly transferred from a desiccator to the upper and lower leaf surfaces, where they are held firmly between two strips of celluloid by means of paper clips, taking care not to damage the tissues in the process of attachment. In this way the paper is protected from atmospheric moisture. A standard shade of pink is set up, by breathing on a portion of the paper and then enclosing it alone between celluloid sheets. The time taken for the hygroscopic strips in contact with the leaf to change to the standard shade is a measure of the rate at which water is being withdrawn from the leaf. The method may thus be used to give an indication of the state of the stomata, and to study the effect of changes in external conditions upon them. There are, however, serious drawbacks in the use of the technique for this last purpose. The paper inevitably shades the leaf, and the assumption has to be made that, over a fairly short experimental period, the stomata are not significantly affected by this. Also, the hygroscopic paper exerts an artificial drying effect, and since it removes moisture rapidly, it is possible that the rate of transpiration might be affected by such factors as the drying-out of the outer layers of the mesophyll cell walls, as discussed on p. 84. Another serious drawback to this type of experiment is that no account can be taken of differences in cuticular transpiration between the two surfaces. In its favour, the method possesses advantages such as quickness, simplicity, the fact that the same leaf may be used for repeated determinations, that intact plants may be used, and that a large number of stomata is covered, so averaging out the effects of individual variations in size.

The most useful application of the cobalt chloride method is in making elementary comparisons of stomatal densities on the two leaf surfaces, although here, one assumes that the average size of the stomata is the same on each.

The method may also be used, in conjunction with microscopic observation, to demonstrate that stomata are the major means of water loss from a leaf. Pieces of epidermis are stripped from the two surfaces, mounted in water, and examined microscopically. The total number of stomata in, say, four different fields of view are counted for each surface. Usually, there is a strong correlation between the ratio of the time taken for the colour change, in the cobalt chloride method, to take place, and the observed stomatal densities, thus demonstrating the importance of the stomata in permitting water loss, as well as the relative impermeability of the cuticle.

(iv) *Porometer methods.* If air is made to flow through a leaf, the rate of flow will be affected by the state of the stomatal apertures. In the simplest type of assembly, the leaf, still attached to the plant, is placed between the broad rim of a small glass chamber (the porometer cup), clamped by rubber bands to a glass slide (Fig. 24). Between the leaf and the rim of the cup is placed a gelatin washer, so as to provide an air-tight seal. The washer is best prepared by allowing a solution of gelatin in hot water to solidify in a shallow dish, and then cutting out a piece of the required size by means of cork-borers. The porometer cup is joined to a vertical tube containing a 'head' of liquid paraffin, which exerts a small suction on the air above it. The rate of fall of the meniscus shows the rate at which air is being drawn through the leaf tissue, entering through the stomata on the part of the leaf's surface not covered by the cup. Since the suction effect decreases as the meniscus falls, the experiment must be repeated over the same range of meniscus levels when the new conditions are being studied. To avoid this difficulty a constant-pressure aspirator may be used instead of a head of liquid in a tube.

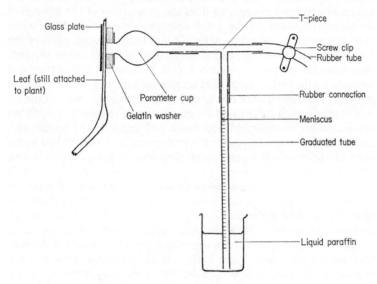

FIG. 24. A simple type of porometer.

A more sensitive instrument is known as the resistance porometer. Here, a stream of air under a constant pressure of just over an atmosphere is forced through the cup, and by means of a system of manometers, the resistance offered by the leaf to the flow is measured, and hence an estimate of the state of the stomatal apertures is obtained. A more complex, but highly sensitive 'Wheatstone bridge porometer' is described by Heath and Russell.[1]

[1] J. Exp. Bot. 2, 111–116 (1951).

In each case, the composition of the air may be controlled, and records can be made on the same area of leaf over long periods. In one type of resistance porometer, records are made automatically. Thousands of stomata are covered by a porometer cup, again averaging out individual variations. It is important that the cup should be detachable between readings, otherwise small changes in carbon dioxide concentration may occur inside it, seriously affecting the stomata (see p. 71). Indeed, it was the fact that stomata in undetached cups often appeared to be wider open than those outside the cups which prompted the investigation by Professor O. V. S. Heath in which the effects of small changes in carbon dioxide level on stomata were first demonstrated.

The resistance of the leaf to the flow of air across it depends not only upon the size of stomatal apertures, but also upon the resistance offered by the mesophyll. This is a distinct drawback, for as the stomatal apertures change, so does the proportion of the mesophyll resistance included in the total resistance measured. Thus when stomata are wide open, less of the air will enter through parts of the leaf remote from the cup, and more through stomata nearer the cup, than when the stomata are nearly closed. With leaves having plenty of stomata on the surface opposite that to which the cup is attached, this difficulty is avoided, since due to their great proximity, most of the air will enter through these at all times. Finally, it should be noted that small changes in mesophyll resistance may occur as the turgor, and hence the size of the cells changes in response to a diminished water content of the leaf. It is important, therefore, to keep the plants well watered.

In addition to the porometers described above, several types of diffusion porometers exist which measure stomatal aperture as reflected by their diffusive capacity rather than by their ability to transmit air under a pressure difference. In one model[1] the cup, containing a proportion of hydrogen, is applied to one side of the leaf, with air on the other. Since hydrogen diffuses faster than air, the pressure inside the cup falls, and the rate at which hydrogen has to be supplied to keep the pressure constant gives a measure of the diffusive capacity of the stomata. Another instrument depends upon the Dufour effect, whereby when two gases at the same temperature mix together, the temperature rises.[2] A small jet of hydrogen is blown against the leaf surface. Some of this diffuses through the leaf, and the rise in temperature which occurs when it meets the air on the other side is detected with the aid of a very delicate and sensitive thermocouple.

[1] Gregory and Armstrong. Proc. Roy. Soc. (Lond.) **B 114**, 27–42 (1946).
[2] J. Exp. Bot. **4**, 283–295 (1953).

3. Factors Affecting Transpiration

The transpiration rate of plants is influenced by two principal factors, firstly the steepness of the diffusion pressure (vapour pressure) gradient between the transpiring surface and the atmosphere, and secondly the size of the stomatal apertures.

(a) **The vapour pressure gradient.** With stomatal size constant, transpiration rates could normally be expected to be proportional to the steepness of the vapour pressure gradient, which depends chiefly upon the humidity and velocity of the external air, and upon the temperatures of both the air and the transpiring surface.

(i) *Humidity.* The diffusion pressure of water vapour in air depends upon the prevailing concentration of water molecules. This concentration is usually expressed by the value of the relative humidity of the air. Relative humidity is the amount of water vapour present in a mass of air at a particular temperature, expressed as a percentage of the maximum amount of vapour which can be held by the same air mass under the same conditions. For example, a value of 100 per cent relative humidity corresponds to complete saturation, the pressure exerted by the vapour at this point being 17.51 mm of mercury, at 20° C. At 85 per cent relative humidity (such as might obtain just after a period of rainfall) the air is 85 per cent saturated, the vapour pressure at this point being 14.92 mm of mercury; again at 20° C. At 50 per cent relative humidity (such as might be found on a day with no rainfall) the corresponding vapour pressure at the same temperature is only 8.76 mm of mercury.

If it is assumed that the air in the mesophyll spaces remains fully saturated throughout (i.e. the relative humidity is always 100 per cent) the possible effect of changes in humidity can readily be calculated. At 85 per cent R.H., the vapour pressure difference between the internal and external atmospheres will be 17.51 − 14.92 = 2.59 mm of mercury. At 50 per cent R.H., however, this becomes 17.51 − 8.76 = 8.75 mm of mercury. Thus if all other factors remain unaltered, with the leaf and air temperature 20° C, a decrease in relative humidity over this range would be expected to increase the transpiration rate more than three-fold.

(ii) *Wind velocity.* Within reasonable limits, an increased wind velocity leads to increased transpiration, mainly because of the decreased tendency for water vapour to accumulate near the leaf surface (see p. 65). Also, mass movements of air through stomata may be brought about (see p.68). On the other hand, it should be realized that air currents may tend to reduce transpiration by minimizing the leaf temperature, although this effect is probably insignificant under average circumstances.

(iii) *Temperature.* Simultaneous increases in air and leaf temperature increase transpiration rates. This is because the vapour pressure of the internal leaf atmosphere increases, whilst that of the atmosphere undergoes little or no increase. As the temperature of a mass of air rises, so does its capacity for holding water vapour. Thus at a given relative humidity, a greater quantity of water vapour is present than at the lower temperature. At 20° C the internal vapour pressure is, as above, 17.51 mm of mercury. At 25° C the value rises to 23.69 mm of mercury, provided that the relative humidity is maintained at 100 per cent by increased evaporation from the mesophyll cells. If the relative humidity of the atmosphere at 20° C is 50 per cent, the vapour pressure is 8.76 mm of mercury, but at 25° C this is virtually unaltered, because although the relative humidity will have fallen considerably, the amount of moisture present is virtually the same as at the lower temperature. Thus, whilst at 20° C the vapour pressure difference is 17.51 − 8.76 = 8.76 mm of mercury, at 25° C this becomes 23.69 − 8.76 = 14.93 mm of mercury. This is an increase of nearly 60 per cent for a 5°C rise in temperature.[1]

The temperature of a plant may be raised above that of its surroundings by the absorption of light, and in direct sunlight the temperature difference may approach 10 deg C. The temperature, humidity and vapour pressure of the air are all unaffected by light, since virtually none is absorbed. The vapour pressure of the leaf's internal atmosphere is, however, increased as in the case described above, leading to a similar marked increase in the transpiration rate.

Apart from affecting the vapour pressure gradient, changes in temperature and light intensity influence transpiration considerably through their effects upon stomata. This aspect is dealt with below.

(b) **Changes in stomatal aperture size.** Since stomatal pores constitute the main means of gaseous exchange between plants and their environment, changes in their dimensions would be expected to affect transpiration rates to a considerable extent. Thus complete closure is normally accompanied by a greatly reduced rate of water loss, and opening by a corresponding increase. It seems likely that stomata are, in fact, situated at that point in the transpiration stream at which they can be most effective in controlling water loss. The justification for this view lies in the fact that the resistance to flow of water vapour

[1] In actual fact, the moisture content, and hence the vapour pressure of the external air, will rise somewhat due to the increased evapotranspiration, so that the vapour pressure difference at the higher temperature will tend to be less than that stated. This effect would only become significant, however, on a still day when there are many evaporating surfaces in the vicinity.

from the leaf to the atmosphere is many times greater than that offered to the flow of water by the whole of the plant's conducting tissue. Thus the stomata control the value of the greatest resistance in the system, and so operate at the most effective point in the chain. This point is further considered in Chapter Six, p. 92.

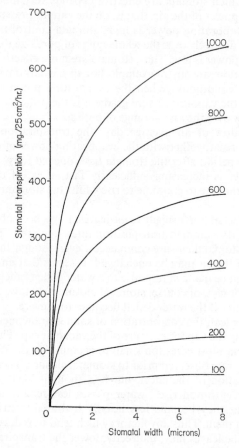

FIG. 25. Relationship between stomatal width and transpiration rate of *Betula pubescens* in quiet air at various levels of atmospheric evaporating power. The rates of evaporation (also in mg/25cm/hour) from a physical surface are given above each curve.[1]

As can be seen from the data presented in Fig. 25, however, stomata exert their greatest degree of control over the smaller range of pore

[1] Adapted from Stålfelt 1932 in *An Introduction to Plant Physiology* by Curtis and Clark. Copyright 1950. McGraw-Hill.

size. Although the transpiration rate is affected to some extent over the whole size range, the effect is overshadowed at the larger pore sizes by the steepness of the vapour pressure gradient, which, as the pore size increases, takes over increasingly as the principal factor controlling transpiration. However, it will also be seen that the size range over which stomata are effective depends very much upon the evaporating power of the air, that is, on the vapour pressure gradient. When the evaporating power is high, stomata control transpiration much more effectively over the whole range of pore size than when the evaporating power is low. Thus, stomata are more effective in altering the transpiration rate on, for example, hot, dry, windy days than under cool, humid conditions. When the evaporating power is poor, the steepness of the vapour pressure gradient is the principal controlling factor, except over the lowest range of pore size.

In the course of an average day, the transpiration rate often continues to rise together with the evaporating power of the air for a considerable period after the stomata have opened fully. If the evaporating power is increasing sufficiently fast, it is, of course, even possible for the rate to continue to rise whilst the stomata are closing.

(c) **The effect of water supply to the leaves.** It has been observed that, especially in the summer, transpiration rates sometimes begin to fall long before stomatal closure commences, even though the evaporating power of the air may be unchanged. It seems that an adjustment to the rate can be made in response to a water deficit independently of stomata, although, of course, stomatal closure may take place before the normal time if the water deficit becomes too severe.

In a drying leaf, the concentration of solutes in the mesophyll cells rises, lowering the vapour pressure of the vacuolar sap. This reduction is, however, in most cases too small to account for the reductions in transpiration rate observed prior to stomatal closure. There is no very clear explanation of the effect, but it is thought likely that, as the osmotic concentration rises, water passes less readily into the cell walls, so that they become less heavily hydrated, restricting evaporation from them. Thus any factors which tend to reduce the supply of water to the leaves may, indirectly, lower the transpiration rate in this way. These factors are, of course, the same as those which can ultimately lead to wilting. The chief ones are listed on p. 107.

4. The Measurement of Transpiration

There can be no entirely satisfactory means of computing the transpiration rate of a plant under entirely natural field conditions, since any experimental procedure inevitably alters the environment to some degree. Often, a method involves the excision of a shoot or leaf, a procedure which radically alters the conditions of water supply to the transpiring regions. Even where whole plants are used, they usually have to be grown in pots or water cultures, so that the roots are far from being under field conditions. However, most methods which are in use can give valuable information as to which environmental factors are the most important ones in relation to water loss.

(a) **Gravimetric methods.** The loss of weight by a plant with its pot over a measured time period gives an accurate measure of the amount of water transpired. The pot must be enclosed in an impervious material such as polythene, so that evaporation can only take place from the plant's surface. Changes in dry weight due to metabolism may be safely ignored over a short experimental period. Parts of plants, standing in tubes of water with a thin layer of oil over the surface, may be treated similarly. For field trials on various types of crops, lysimeters are employed. Large vessels containing soil and plants are sunk into the ground, and weighed periodically. Water loss can then be found for crops under near-natural field conditions. Such measurements find application in, for example, computing the irrigation requirements for a given crop plant in a particular region.

(b) **Hygrometric methods.** In one of the most sensitive procedures, two identical streams of air are passed into separate, weighed tubes, containing phosphorus pentoxide or anhydrous calcium chloride, to absorb all water vapour. One stream passes first over the transpiring material, and from the difference in the gains in weight of the two tubes, the amount of vapour transpired during the period and under the conditions of the experiment may be determined. These conditions are likely to be very different from those encountered in the field.

The cobalt chloride technique (see p. 77) is also sometimes used for the purpose of comparing the transpiration rates from two or more surfaces. A comparison may be made between the upper and lower surfaces of a single leaf, or between the leaves of two or more plants. It must be borne in mind that the hygroscopic paper exerts a strong desiccating influence upon the leaf, and also that the leaf is inevitably shaded. Thus the amount of water transpired may be very different from the amount which would have been lost if the conditions prior to the experiment had been maintained.

(c) **Potometric methods.** A potometer is an instrument designed to measure the rate of water absorption by a plant or part of a plant. In plants which are, or have been, rapidly transpiring, the rate of water uptake may furnish little or no information as to the transpiration rate (see p. 98). If, however, the conditions are such that the transpiration rate is not excessive, the two may well bear a constant relationship with one another, although they are probably seldom exactly equal.

D

Under such circumstances changes in the rate of uptake may legitimately be used to compare the effect of changed conditions upon the transpiration rate.

Some of the larger potometers, such as the well-known Farmer's model, are capable of accommodating entire plants which have been grown in water cultures, so as to avoid damage to the root system by digging up. Perhaps the most serious objection here is that the reservoir is so large that the instrument acts as a water thermometer, even a small temperature change being sufficient to cause great inaccuracies due to the expansion of the water and its container. Such instruments are much more suitable for class demonstration purposes at an elementary level than for accurate measurements.

Smaller, more sensitive instruments are suitable for detailed observations over short periods, using detached leaves or small shoots. If such an instrument is hung from a sensitive balance, simultaneous determination of the rate of uptake and the rate of transpiration may be carried out by a careful operator. One easily constructed assembly is shown in Fig. 26. The rate of uptake is indicated by the movement of

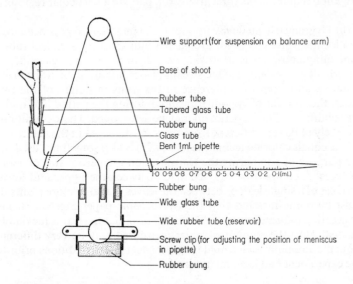

Wire support (for suspension on balance arm)

Base of shoot

Rubber tube
Tapered glass tube
Rubber bung
Glass tube
Bent 1 ml. pipette

1·0 0·9 0·8 0·7 0·6 0·5 0·4 0·3 0·2 0·1 (ml.)

Rubber bung
Wide glass tube
Wide rubber tube (reservoir)
Screw clip (for adjusting the position of meniscus in pipette)
Rubber bung

FIG. 26. Apparatus for simultaneous determination of transpiration rate and absorption rate.

the meniscus in the graduated pipette, and the rate of loss by the progressive decrease in weight. The two rates are often found to be widely different under conditions favouring high transpiration rates, especially when whole, intact plants are used. Various types of seedling shoots are suitable material. As in all potometric work, the shoots must be cut under water to avoid the formation of air locks in the xylem. The complete assembly is set up under, and filled with freshly boiled and cooled water, and should be left to equilibrate for a day before readings are commenced. (During this time, a length of water-filled rubber tubing leading to a beaker of water should be attached to the pipette, so that air does not enter the apparatus.) It is also possible to combine potometer readings with those of a porometer, and so examine any correlation between stomatal aperture size and water uptake rates.

5. The 'Uses' of Transpiration

It is usual to regard transpiration as the inevitable, but undesirable result of the construction and metabolic requirements of the plant. It is undesirable in that plants often suffer severe setbacks to their development, or are even killed, as a result of excessive water loss. Also, large areas of the Earth's surface support only a very restricted flora, due to the fact that although there may be sufficient water to maintain metabolism and even to allow active growth, at least during certain seasons, there is insufficient water available to replace transpirational losses.

Transpiration is an obvious and widespread phenomenon and investigators and speculators have, from time to time, put forward 'mitigating circumstances' which might lift transpiration from its role as a menace to one of distinct usefulness, or indeed indispensability. There is, however, no real evidence to support the view that transpiration does, in fact, fulfil any function in plants which would not proceed adequately in the absence of the process. There are effects associated with transpiration which may, at times, serve a limited useful purpose, but such effects are purely incidental, and only very exceptionally might they be essential to the life of the plant. Three such effects merit some discussion.

The first springs from the fact that whenever a gram of water vaporizes, about 540 calories of latent heat are absorbed from the evaporating surface. This inevitable lowering of the leaf temperature has been seized upon by some as a significant factor in permitting the survival of plants growing under very hot climatic conditions. The available evidence, however, suggests that the maximum lowering of the temperature which could be effected in this way would rarely approach 5° C. This assumes maximum rates of transpiration, which are most unlikely to occur under very hot conditions, due to regulation by the plant. Those conditions which would be most likely to bring about overheating and desiccation of the tissues would tend to bring into play stomatal closure, or other restricting influences, so that it is most unlikely that transpiration acts as a protective mechanism. Excessive transpiration rates are, in general, more hazardous to plants by way of desiccation than beneficial because of any slight cooling effect which they may bring about. It is, however, just conceivable that in the unlikely event of exceptionally hot conditions co-existing with an abundance of soil water, so that transpiration losses may be made good, the cooling effect might be of marginal survival value.

Another effect of transpiration often held to be beneficial is that, since the process actuates an upward movement of water from the soil, high transpiration rates favour increased absorption of salts, and their distribution within the plant. As we shall see in Chapter Six, however, the main water uptake process is a passive physical one, deriving its energy from the evaporating power of the atmosphere. Salt uptake, on the other hand, derives its energy from respiration, and is therefore dependent upon metabolism. In the main, therefore, the two processes are independent of each other. There is, though, a small component of salt uptake which is passive, and probably associated with water uptake. This small component will increase whenever the rate of water uptake increases, leading to some acceleration in the total salt uptake. In addition, the upward transport of salts in the transpiration stream, once they have been absorbed, can hardly be avoided. There is no evidence whatever, though, that either salt uptake or transport does not take place adequately when transpiration rates are low, or even nil. Careful experiments in which plants kept under conditions of high humidity have been compared with similar rapidly transpiring specimens, have shown that the former suffer no adverse effects. Indeed, from standpoints such as growth rate and speed of maturation of fruit, their development is often enhanced. Thus any effect of transpiration on the uptake or movement of salts is purely incidental, and in no way essential to development.

Finally, it is sometimes claimed that since transpiration causes water to rise into the shoot system, it allows the meristematic cells at the apex to be supplied, and is essential for the expansion of newly formed cells. The fallacy here is very obvious. Any part of a plant whose diffusion pressure deficit becomes greater than that of neighbouring regions will receive water from them, so that water movement through the xylem to the meristems could be actuated quite adequately by the imbibitional diffusion pressure deficits which develop in the cytoplasm of the cells, without any 'assistance' from transpiration. In fact, of course, far from assisting the activity of meristems, transpiration competes with them for the available water, and for this reason growth rates and transpiration rates are often inversely related.

REFERENCES

'Light and carbon dioxide in stomatal movements', Heath. Encyclopaedia of plant physiology, Vol. XVII/1, 415–464 (1960).

'The influence of water strain on the minimum intercellular space carbon dioxide concentration and stomatal movement in wheat leaves', Heath and Meidner. J. Exp. Bot., **12**, 35, 226–242 (1961).

'Stomatal physiology', H. J. Ketellapper, Ann. Rev. Plant Physiol. **14** (1963).

CHAPTER SIX

The Absorption and Ascent of Water

Clearly, transpired water must be replaced from the environment. The means by which this is achieved has been the subject of much research, and even more speculation. According to the most widely held present-day view, the uptake of water from the soil, and its ascent in plants, is actuated principally by the transpiration process itself, although other factors probably play an additional role. The main flow of water through a plant is therefore referred to as the transpiration stream. The operation of this stream will be discussed first, and then miscellaneous problems related to uptake and distribution of water generally will be considered.

1. The Transpiration Stream

(a) **General.** The transpiration stream originates at the evaporating surfaces of the leaf mesophyll cells. The saturated walls of these cells may be compared with a lampwick, in that when liquid is removed, more takes its place. The water content is maintained by imbibitional and capillary forces. As transpiration proceeds, water flows through the cell wall, and the diffusion pressure deficit of the vacuolar contents of the transpiring cells increases. As a result, an osmotic flow of water takes place from neighbouring cells, and the effect is propagated from cell-to-cell as outlined on p. 37, to which the reader should refer. Water flows into cells of higher D.P.D. from those whose D.P.D. is less. In the leaf, a series of perhaps only three or four mesophyll cells is involved before a fine vascular trace is reached. Quite apart from a purely osmotic cell-to-cell transport of water, it is likely that some travels to the transpiring surface from the xylem entirely by capillarity within the cell wall materials, without entering cytoplasm or vacuoles. Also, some may travel entirely within the cytoplasm via plasmodesmata. The amount of water travelling by these alternative pathways is likely to be insignificant however.

Withdrawal of water from the fine xylem elements into the leaf parenchyma results in the upward passage of the liquid in the water-filled conducting elements which, as we have seen (p. 46) form a continuous system throughout the plant, including the root system. The forces tending to pull water upwards in this way are opposed by the weight of water in the columns, the frictional resistance offered by the walls of the conducting channels, and the resistance of the root

90

tissue and soil particles. However, so long as the tendency to draw water into the leaf cells (i.e. their D.P.D.) exceeds these opposing forces, the flow will continue. In effect, water is dragged upwards through the xylem elements under a tension which is transmitted throughout the entire system. The tension is, of course, due to the fact that the water is being subjected to two opposing sets of forces – those tending to draw water into the leaves, and those frictional, gravitational and other forces tending to prevent the flow. In the root, a cell-to-cell movement of water takes place in a similar way to that in the leaf. As water passes into the vessels and tracheids of the stele from the cells of the pericycle and endodermis, these experience an increased D.P.D., so that an osmotic flow takes place involving the cells of the cortex, and finally the root hairs. When the D.P.D. of the hairs exceeds the forces holding water around the soil particles, uptake occurs. By no means all the water enters via root hairs however; any thin-walled cells in contact with the soil can carry out absorption. Also, as in the case of leaves, some transport of water probably takes place within cell walls and cytoplasm, without entering vacuoles. Thus a diffusion pressure gradient may be visualized throughout the course of the transpiration stream, maintained by the evaporative power of the atmosphere, which provides the 'engine' for water transport.

(b) **The problem of tall trees.** In tall trees, the columns of water must be so extensive as to require very large forces to support and move them against frictional and gravitational resistance. Clearly, if a mechanism such as that just outlined can be shown to be adequate for the flow of the transpiration stream in these extreme cases, there should be no difficulty in accounting for the process in plants of more lowly stature.

The tallest present-day trees are the Californian redwoods (*Sequoia sempervirens*) and the Australian Blue Gum trees (*Eucalyptus regnans*). The height record for a living tree seems to be held by a redwood in Humbolt County, California, U.S.A. In 1963, this was reported to be 367.8 feet tall. There are no really reliable records of trees in the past having reached such a height, so that this may be an all-time height record. In Great Britain, the tallest trees are Silver Firs and Douglas Firs, of which specimens of well over 180 feet exist. Pines, Spruces, Limes and Elms of 150 feet and over also occur.

To support the weight of a column of water, say, 400 feet high, a force of (400–34)/34 atmospheres is necessary in addition to atmospheric pressure (which is equivalent to a 34-foot head of water). The force needed to overcome the frictional resistance offered by the conducting tissue must be added to this. Dixon found that, in an actively transpiring *Taxus* plant, this would be about the same as the force necessary to support the water columns when motionless. This may not be a valid principle for all plants, since values obtained more recently by other workers for various types of trees indicate that only rarely does the frictional resistance approach the value of the force necessary to support the columns. Assuming, however, that Dixon's estimate applies to a hypothetical 400-foot tree, the force necessary in the leaves now becomes $2 \times (400-34)/34$ atmospheres, or about 22 atmospheres. To this must be added a few atmospheres to overcome the forces holding water in the soil, and the resistance of the root tissue to the lateral transport of water across it from the root hairs to the stele. This force will vary greatly, but with a reasonably moist soil it might be of the order of 5 atmospheres, bringing the total to about 27 atmospheres. The cells of the leaf mesophyll must have D.P.D.s of at least this magnitude if water is to be absorbed by them from the xylem elements. The D.P.D. of the atmosphere itself is usually very large. It has been calculated, for example, that (neglecting frictional forces) with a relative humidity as high as 99 per cent, the atmosphere could withdraw water from a column as high as 430 feet, since even at this moisture level the atmosphere has a D.P.D. of about 14 atmospheres. Air to 80 per cent relative humidity has a D.P.D. of about 300 atmospheres. Thus it will be apparent that, under normal circumstances, there is sufficient evaporative power available in the atmosphere to abstract water from the tallest plants.

A general, but highly approximate, idea of the magnitude of the D.P.D.s that might sometimes exist in an actively transpiring 400-foot-high tree growing in a moist soil, is given in Fig. 27. The values shown are entirely speculative and theoretical, and are given solely for illustrative purposes. The actual situation in a particular plant will vary from minute to minute, according to variations in the many complex and interacting factors which can affect transpiration, the state of soil moisture, and the general activity of the plant.

One important point which the values shown do illustrate is that the D.P.D. difference between the atmosphere and the transpiring leaf cells (300 minus 28 atmospheres) is many times greater than that between the soil water and the leaf (28 minus 1 atmospheres). Now, under average circumstances, the rates of transpiration, and the rates of water uptake and conduction, are roughly equal. This means that the resistance to flow at the leaf/air surface must accordingly be many times greater than the total resistance offered by the rest of the conducting system. Thus the plant's main control over the transpiration rate (the stomata) operates at the most effective point in the system, i.e. the point at which the largest resistance in the chain may be altered. This was referred to in Chapter Five, p. 82. It also means that damage to the conducting tissue of a plant would have to be very considerable in order to have an appreciable effect upon the speed at which water travels to the leaves, since here the resistance to flow is relatively small.

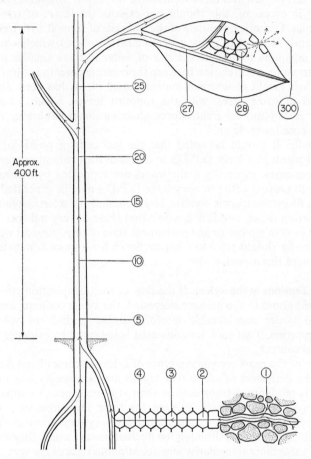

FIG. 27. Diagram to illustrate possible diffusion pressure deficits at various points in the hydrostatic system of a 400-ft tree, with readily available soil water, and a relative humidity of 80%.

In view of the large forces needed to move water upwards in very tall trees, the vacuolar contents of their leaf cells would be expected to have high osmotic potentials, for if turgor is to be maintained (i.e. if there is to be a positive wall pressure maintained) the osmotic potential must exceed the D.P.D. of the cells, as can be seen from the relationship D.P.D. = O.P. − W.P. derived earlier (p. 27). Unfortunately no data appear to be available for *Sequoia*. Values of up to about 50 atmospheres have been reported for the cells of the leathery leaves of some xerophytes, and there seems to be no reason why values as high as, or in excess of, this should not exist in the leaves of trees like Sequoias. Osmotic potentials of the leaf cells of some British trees are frequently found to be of the order of 20 atmospheres, which would be quite adequate to actuate the rise of water in these smaller plants. Furthermore, a correlation between the osmotic potential of leaf cells, and their height of insertion on individual plants has been demonstrated in some cases, with the topmost leaves, which would be expected to require a greater force, showing somewhat higher values than those lower down.

Finally, it should be noted that the leaf cells of physiologically wilted plants can have D.P.D.s in excess of their osmotic potentials. In these cases, especially if the leaves are supported by mechanical tissue to prevent collapse, very large D.P.D.s may be generated. The leaves of gymnosperms contain large amounts of sclerenchymatous supporting tissue, and it is possible that those of very tall specimens might exist in a more or less permanent state of physiological wilting. The reader should refer to Chapter Seven for a more complete discussion of this aspect.

(c) **Tensions in the xylem.** If the flow of the transpiration stream is brought about in the manner suggested, the xylem contents must be placed under considerable tensions during periods of vigorous transpiration. That such tensions exist is indicated by evidence from several sources.

One of the most convincing types of evidence comes from the fact that the diameters of many tree trunks are measurably less during periods of vigorous transpiration than at other times. An apparatus known as a dendrograph is used for these measurements, which employs a temperature-compensated lever system to magnify the changes in diameter. Although the fluctuations are small, they show a remarkable diurnal regularity when continuous records are kept over a period of several days. The reduction in diameter is presumed to be due to a slight constriction of the individual xylem elements as the hydrostatic tensions within them increase with the transpiration rate as the day goes on.

Tensions in the xylem of tree trunks may also be demonstrated in the following way. A Plasticine cup is attached to the side of the trunk of a rapidly transpiring tree, and a little red dye, such as eosin, is poured into it. With a brace and bit a boring is made under the surface of the liquid, through the bark and into the outer layers of xylem. Usually, some of the liquid can be seen to disappear instantly from the cup. The bit is wiped clean, and fresh borings are made at intervals vertically above the original one. By the stained appearance of the emerging shavings, an estimate may be made of the distance of penetration of the dye. When such experiments are performed on tall trees, it is easily possible to demonstrate a rapid rise of several feet. Not all of such rises can, however, be claimed to be due to the instantaneous release of tensions, since it takes a little time to make the borings, by which time dye has been carried up further in the normal transpiration stream.

In the case of some herbaceous plants, especially those of the *Cucurbitaceae*, in which the vessels are exceptionally wide and near to the surface, it has proved possible, by careful microdissection, to examine individual vessels in intact, actively transpiring plants. If a vessel is ruptured under mercury by a needle point, the columns of water can be seen to rupture violently, in a manner consistent with the presence of a tension therein, and mercury enters. It has also been observed that the thin portions of the walls of protoxylem elements (i.e. the unlignified parts) are frequently pulled inwards in transpiring plants as indicated in Fig. 17.

In many cases, observed rates of water movement can only be accounted for on the basis of the existence in the water columns of forces far in excess of those which could be due to atmospheric pressure alone, thus indicating that there must be either 'pumping' from below, or traction from above. Measurements of the velocity of the transpiration stream may be obtained without disrupting the xylem conduits, by applying a heating device to the stem (usually an electric element) and measuring the time taken for the warmed contents to reach a sensitive thermocouple some distance above. Velocities in excess of three feet per minute have been recorded.

The transpiration stream may be simulated in the laboratory by fastening a leafy twig to a long, vertical, glass tube filled with water, and dipping into a trough containing mercury. For a successful experiment it is essential that tremendous care is devoted to the exclusion of air from the system. A plant with little pith (which often contains much air) must be used. Gymnosperms are the most suitable, probably partly because any small air-lock in the tracheids is quickly isolated (see p. 53). The twig is cut under water, and the bark removed from the lower part to which the tubing will be attached. The cut part must never be allowed to contact the air. As far as possible, all the subsequent operations should be performed under water, in, for example, a large sink. The base of the twig is placed in boiling distilled water for a full hour, to expel any air, protecting the foliage from the steam. A tight-fitting length of new rubber tubing is now attached, and the glass tube is subsequently fitted. The latter must have been flushed and then filled with boiling water from a nearby flask, and the contents allowed to cool, remembering that the water will contract slightly. This can be a somewhat complex operation, but it need not be so if the student thinks out carefully at each stage what he is going to do next. Some short lengths of rubber tubing and a couple of screw clips will be found useful, and the assistance of a second person is essential. When fitted to the twig, the glass tube has its open end (still under water) placed in a trough of mercury. The whole assembly can then be lifted clear of the sink, and supported in a convenient part of the laboratory. If capillary tubing is used, the results may be available in about three hours. Wide glass tubing is, however, more readily flushed with the boiling water, and easier to obtain in an air-free state. In this case, the results may take several days to become apparent, due to the greater quantity of water which must be absorbed before the mercury can reach the required height. Rises of up to 118 cm of mercury have been obtained from this procedure, but eventually air enters the system, usually having been sucked from other regions of the twig, and the column breaks. In order for a head of mercury 118 cm to be supported, a tension of at least half an atmosphere must have existed in the rising column. Although a tension of this sort would be totally inadequate to support a tall column of water in a tree, it is wholly reasonable to suppose that, with intact xylem, into which air cannot easily enter, very much higher tensions can be maintained.

If the transpiring regions are to be supplied at the required rate, a considerable number of unbroken water columns must be maintained. When the contents are subjected to great tension, it would seem likely that air, once introduced into the xylem, would quickly expand to block many of the conducting channels. Tracheids which became blocked with air would very quickly be isolated by pit aspiration (p. 53) so that the air-lock would not spread extensively, but in the case of vessels, a much larger conducting region would be affected, because of their greater length. There is no doubt that in most angiosperm trees, many of the older xylem elements do contain air, and so have ceased to function for water conduction. The most recently formed elements are, however, invariably water-filled, and are easily capable of delivering water to the leaves in sufficient quantity, and at the required rate. In experiments carried out by Preston on a 60-year-old beech, 20 cm in diameter, it was found from the observed rates of water loss and rates of movement in the trunk that a band of the most recently formed xylem only half a centimetre wide could account for all of the water travelling upwards. In this connection, it is noteworthy that, whilst forest trees increase in girth in each year of their life, increases in height almost cease after a certain size has been reached. This is because of the constant need for new, intact, water columns. In other experiments, Preston showed that even if all the conducting elements of a tree with young foliage were severed (this he achieved by making two overlapping saw-cuts a few inches apart from opposite directions) the developing foliage showed only transient ill effects, although a few leaves were lost. Within a few days, before serious wilting had had time to take place, sufficient new xylem had been formed by cambial activity over a course avoiding the cuts, to adequately supply the aerial parts. In the meantime the plant must have survived on water contained in cell vacuoles, together with that brought up from the roots within cell wall capillaries.

One of the major points of discussion in relation to transpiration has concerned the magnitude of the cohesive forces between water molecules, and, in particular, whether they are large enough to resist the tensions likely to be encountered. There is some disagreement as to these points, in spite of the many investigations which have been carried out. On theoretical grounds, the tensile strength of water has been calculated to be of the order of 210,000 lb per sq. in, or well over 1,400 atmospheres. These theoretical maximum values could not be expected to be attained in practice, owing to inevitable imperfections in the configuration of the water molecules, and to the presence of dissolved gases. Values obtained experimentally seem to depend so much upon the particular technique used, that it is conceivable that none of these values is relevant to the actual conditions inside intact plants. It has been claimed that a tension of over 200 atmospheres can be successfully withstood under experimental conditions, a value more than adequate to meet the demands made by the tallest trees, or by severely wilted plants. On the other hand, values as low as 40 atmospheres have been arrived at, and if these lower values are the true ones, serious difficulties arise in explaining the ascent of water in very tall trees on the basis of the cohesion-tension theory outlined earlier.

With regard to the magnitude of the adhesive forces between the walls of the xylem elements and their contents, there is general agreement that these are very large indeed, perhaps in excess of 1,000 atmospheres. Neither is there any serious doubt of the ability of the lignified walls of vessels and tracheids to resist very large inward pulls, although, as has been mentioned (p. 94) some contraction in diameter seems to take place when vigorous transpiration is proceeding. The less heavily lignified protoxylem elements probably do not experience large tensions, since they function only for a limited period, in the early stages of development.

2. The Relationship Between Transpiration and Water Uptake

If the transpiration stream is actuated in the manner suggested, transpiration rates and uptake rates would be expected to ce strongly correlated. That this is, in fact, the case is indicated by the date presented in Fig. 28. Generally, transpiration approaches the maximum for a few hours from about noon. The rate falls steeply early in the evening, and is minimal during the hours of darkness. The rate climbs steadily from early morning to about noon. Although water uptake mirrors this diurnal periodicity, it falls considerably behind transpiration, especially as the latter approaches its peak. The data presented in Fig. 28 were obtained for sunflower plants growing in nutrient solutions. In many such determinations, the peak absorption rate is found to occur one to two hours after the peak transpiration rate. It will be seen that a water deficit is incurred by the plant for a period, and this is consistent with the idea of water being dragged through the plant against the resistance offered by various parts of the system. Evidence in further support of this conception is provided by dendrograph measurements, which have shown that, in some cases, the diurnal reduction in diameter of tree trunks (p. 94) takes place in the topmost regions slightly before the effect appears near the bole. Also, when the transpiration rate, as measured by the thermocouple method, begins to increase during the morning, it again does so first in the more elevated regions. It seems that by far the greatest contribution to the plant's resistance to water movement is due to the cortical cells of the root.

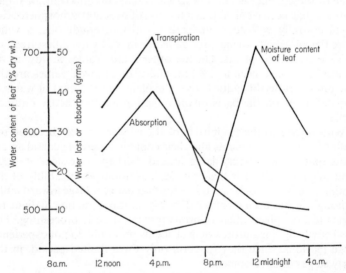

FIG. 28. Relationship between leaf moisture content, absorption and transpiration in sunflower plants grown in a nutrient solution.[1]

The actual difference between the rates of uptake and transpiration depends, of course, upon the actual levels of the two processes which

[1] Kramer, Am. Jour. Bot. 24, 10–15, (1937).

the prevailing conditions will permit. On a hot, windy day, for example, when transpiration is favoured, the discrepancy may be considerable, especially if the soil is dry. On a still, humid day, on the other hand, there may be little difference between the two. When the transpiration rate drops from a high level to a very low one as, for example, at night, water uptake normally still proceeds, so that the water deficit built up is reduced or eliminated.

3. Other Factors Involved in Water Uptake and Transport

Although water uptake and transport are governed chiefly by water loss, there are several means by which water may be absorbed and moved which have no connection with transpiration. For example, in rapidly enlarging regions, such as are present near the apices of stems and roots, and in developing leaves, flowers, and fruits, imbibitional forces come into play, causing an influx of water from other parts of the plant. Such forces will effectively add to the D.P.D. of the xylem contents, and so play a part in absorbing water from the soil. It has already been mentioned that the growth rates of rapidly transpiring plants tend to be considerably lower than those of the same plants when under humid conditions. This is presumably due to the fact that the leaves compete more strongly for the available water when transpiration rates are high.

One of the most widely known factors which has become associated with the uptake of water by plants is that known as **root pressure**. Root pressure is usually demonstrated by attaching a glass tube to the stump of a strong, freshly decapitated tomato, vine or *Fuchsia* plant, by means of a tightly fitting rubber connection. A little water, which may be coloured with a dye, is introduced into the tube, and the level marked. Usually, if the roots are well watered, the liquid will rise slowly in the tube. The flow is greatest in warm conditions, and following a period of high light intensity, so that in nature it is best in the spring. The 'bleeding' of many plants when injured during this season is usually attributable to root pressure. There is a marked diurnal periodicity, the pressure being greatest in the daytime, and lowest at night. The pressure may be measured by attaching a mercury manometer to the stump. As has been indicated, the actual values are extremely variable, but it is most exceptional for 2 atmospheres to be reached, even under the most favourable circumstances. In many plants, root pressure cannot be demonstrated at all. The volume of liquid exuded bears little or no relationship to the pressure exerted, so that 'bleeding' of a cut stem may continue for a long period even though the demonstrable root pressure may be low.

The underlying mechanism of root pressure seems to rest principally upon the absorption of mineral salts from the soil, and their secretion into the xylem. This increases the osmotic potential of the xylem contents, and leads to an influx of water from the much more dilute soil solution. The root cells act, in effect, as a single differentially permeable membrane. As was indicated in Chapter Two, the process of salt uptake depends upon a supply of respiratory energy, and it is therefore not surprising that root pressure is diminished or eliminated by starving the roots of oxygen, or by supplying respiratory inhibitors. It also suggests an explanation of the enhancing effects of increased temperature or high light intensities on root pressure.

Root pressure can be eliminated, at least temporarily, by bathing the roots in a solution of an osmotically active substance. It is found, however, that the osmotic potential of the solution just necessary to prevent exudation is always slightly higher than that of the exudate itself. Two possible explanations of this are that either some of the salts secreted into the xylem are absorbed into other parts before reaching the cut surface, or that there is a metabolic pumping of water from the soil into the xylem quite independently of and in addition to the osmotic flow of water brought about by salt secretion. Whether either of these explanations is correct is not known. It will be recalled that in Chapter Three it was indicated that water uptake into tissues could be influenced by metabolic activity, and indeed it seems that root pressure is a manifestation of such a process of active uptake, so that the discussion which was entered into on p. 35 is largely applicable.

Whatever its detailed mechanism, it is clear that active uptake cannot play any major role in the uptake and ascent of large quantities of water into rapidly transpiring plants, especially in the case of tall species. The root pressures exerted by the majority of plants even under the optimum conditions would be totally inadequate to push water upwards for more than a few feet. Further, with the possible exception of one or two tropical species, the maximum rates of exudation of liquid are far below the normal rates of water conduction and loss. The term 'root pressure' ceases to have any real meaning in the case of rapidly transpiring plants, for here, considerable tensions exist in the water columns, so that if the xylem is tapped, water, far from being exuded, may be rapidly absorbed (see p. 94). Indeed, in intact transpiring plants, it is difficult to demonstrate any active component of water uptake. Other evidence for the relative unimportance of active uptake comes from the observation that detopped plants, in which the 'transpiration pull' does not exist, cannot absorb water from a soil whose D.P.D. is greater than 2 atmospheres, whereas intact plants can do so until the D.P.D. is as much as 15 atmospheres. In the case of some low-growing plants, root pressure could cause water to rise in the stem during periods of low transpiration rates, and this is probably particularly true of many plants which grow in tropical rain forests, where an extremely humid atmosphere prevails. Thus, whenever transpiration is restricted, and soil and climatic conditions favour root pressure, the effect may be strong enough to bring about the exudation of liquid water from the leaf margins. This is known as **guttation** (see p. 102).

Another point of discussion has centred around the question of whether or not forces of capillarity and/or imbibition, operating within the wall substance of xylem elements could play any part in the ascent of water. The answer here is that whilst the available imbibitional and capillary forces may exceed 1,000 atmospheres, the resistance to flow through materials in this way, through such minute channels, is so great that only very small quantities of liquid could pass in a given time. Thus, if conduction within the wall material takes place at all, it cannot supply water at anything approaching the requisite rate. As we shall see in Chapter Seven the movement of water through soil 'capillaries' also occurs extremely slowly. Experimental support for the fact that conduction takes place chiefly within the lumina of the xylem elements comes from the observation that when the lumina only are blocked by wax, cut shoots wilt rapidly, whilst controls remain fresh. Also, if the lumina are constricted in suitable cases, by applying spring clips around the stem, wilting can be induced, recovery rapidly taking place when the constraint is removed. Capillary rise in the lumina of vessels or tracheids can be completely ruled out as an important factor in the ascent of water, for even in the narrowest tracheids it could account for rises of only up to about five feet, and again there would be considerable resistance to flow in these finer tubes.

The final topic in this section concerns the possibility that the living cells of the xylem parenchyma, as distinct from those of the root, which are in intimate and frequent contact with the conducting elements (p. 56) are in some way involved in the ascent of water in plants. So far, we have considered the xylem as fulfilling a merely passive physical role, as a series of conduits along which water travels between various parts of a plant in directions governed by the diffusion pressure deficits of the regions. At the present time, the majority of plant physiologists favour such a viewpoint as providing a reasonable working hypothesis to account for water transport. There are some, however, who maintain that the living xylem parenchyma cells may well have some vital part to play in the process, a part which again depends upon active metabolism. Many early workers, notable amongst whom was Priestley, claimed that conduction was due almost entirely to some sort of pumping action on the part of the living cells. Most of the experiments which have been carried out in this field have involved killing or reducing the metabolic activity of lengths of stem by means of poisons, or extremes of temperature, and examining the effect of the treatment upon the foliage. In all cases, wilting sets in sooner or later, seemingly supporting the idea of a metabolic requirement. The results are, however, readily explicable on the basis of the formation of gummy substances from the injured cytoplasm which block the conduits, and the formation of bulbous outgrowths called tyloses from xylem parenchyma cells, which are known to occlude adjacent xylem elements near the site of an injury. That such an explanation could be correct is supported by the time lag, often of several days, between the application of the treatment, and the onset of wilting. We cannot, however, completely dismiss the possibility that living cells do play some part in the functioning of xylem which is not yet understood.

4. Internal Redistribution of Water

In general, water flows through plant tissues towards regions whose D.P.D. exceeds the general level. Although the bulk of the flow is towards leaves, it has already been noted that, for example, water may be diverted towards rapidly growing regions as a result of imbibitional D.P.D.s. Also, any redistribution of solutes will tend to bring about a redistribution of water by osmotic means.

Daily fluctuations in D.P.D. are commonplace in plant organs, especially the leaves, where there is a marked increase during the daytime, and a fall at night. The daily increase results from both the increase in the amount of solutes following from photosynthesis, and the loss of water by transpiration. Bartholomew[1] has recorded diurnal variations in the dimensions of lemon fruits, which increase at night, and decrease in the daytime. This indicates that the fruit acts as a reservoir from which water can flow towards the leaves in response to an increase in their D.P.D. Similarly, Chandler[2] found that when young succulent fruits were cut from the tree, the fruits withered, even when covered with wax, long before the leaves. If, however, the fruits were allowed to develop fully before the branches were severed, the leaves withered much earlier. This was found to be correlated with the much higher osmotic potential of the cell contents of the mature fruit, so that water could be withdrawn from them by the leaves much less readily than in the unripened state.

5. Guttation

Guttation is the loss of water in liquid form from uninjured plants, and is undoubtedly another manifestation of root pressure (see p. 99). It occurs very commonly in herbaceous species in this country, particularly the grasses. The drops of 'dew' frequently encountered amongst grassland early in the morning often result from guttation,

---

[1] Bartholomew. 'Internal decline of lemons: Water deficit in lemon fruits caused by excessive leaf evaporation'. Am. Jour. Bot., **13**: 102–117 (1926).
[2] 'Sap studies with horticultural plants'. Univ. Mo. Agr. Ex. St. Res. Bul. **14**, 489–552 (1914).

and not from condensation of atmospheric water vapour. The most favourable conditions for guttation are a warm, moist, soil, favouring high root pressure, combined with a cool, still, humid atmosphere favouring a low rate of transpiration, so that water uptake exceeds evaporation. As might be expected, guttation can usually be brought to a halt by applying solutions of osmotically active substances to the roots, so impairing water uptake.

The excess water appears through special water pores, called **hydathodes**, which are generally modified stomata, with unthickened and permanently open 'guard cells'. Beneath the pore is a large group of modified mesophyll cells called the epithem, with large intercellular spaces. Thus water travelling from nearby tracheids finds its way out without encountering much resistance. Usually, hydathodes are situated at the margin of leaves, especially at the tips of any 'teeth' that may be present. In grasses they are found at the tips of the leaves. The most prolific producers of liquid are the Aroids, of the genus *Colocasia*, which grow in humid rain forests. At certain times, water is said to drip so continuously from the pointed tips of the leaves that the effect of a moderate rainfall is produced on the ground below.

Some plants have special water-secreting structures, similar to nectaries, in which quite a different mechanism is involved. Here, there is active metabolic secretion of water by a definite glandular tissue, usually in the form of a short hair, whereas exudation from hydathodes depends simply upon excess hydrostatic pressure in the xylem contents. Secretion from such glands is inhibited by the application of metabolic poisons such as chloroform and cyanide, which depress respiration.

In each case, the liquid which is exuded or secreted may contain solutes, such as mineral salts and amino acids, so that when it evaporates, deposits remain behind. Chalky deposits often incrust the leaves of Saxifrages, and glutamine-rich substances may accumulate on the leaves of certain grasses. Such deposits may provide a suitable habitat for the growth of micro-organisms.

Guttation may be readily demonstrated by covering many kinds of seedlings with a bell jar or polythene sheeting and placing them in warm surroundings. Grasses, notably maize seedlings, are particularly favourable subjects for this, but many mature plants such as *Nasturtium*, Tomato and Vine are vigorous 'guttators' when the conditions are right.

REFERENCES

'How Sap Moves in Trees', M. H. Zimmerman. Scientific American **208**, No. 3 (March, 1963).

CHAPTER SEVEN

Water in the Environment

1. The Hydrologic Cycle

Under the influence of temperature variations, water changes its state with considerable readiness, and as a result, circulates with great mobility. The main pathway is from oceans to atmosphere, thence to land, and then back to ocean and atmosphere. The principal features of this hydrologic cycle, in which vegetation plays an important part, are included in Fig. 29.

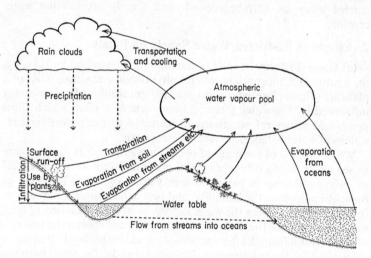

FIG. 29. The principal features of the hydrologic cycle.

Precipitated water falls either as rain, or as ice crystals which subsequently melt. A small part of the water intercepted by foliage evaporates directly, without reaching the ground. The liquid which reaches the soil either infiltrates, or flows over the surface into streams as 'surface run-off'. The relative extents of infiltration and surface run-off depend upon many features, chief of which are the texture and type of soil, and the intensity and duration of precipitation. Run-off is the cause of water erosion, a process especially marked where the soil is bare of plant growth. Much of the infiltrating water is absorbed by vegetation, virtually all of this returning to the atmosphere as transpired vapour. A very small amount evaporates directly from the soil. The remainder, often a substantial proportion of the total, is lost in deep percolation, and contributes to the raising of the water table, the level of which constantly fluctuates. Eventually this water finds its way into streams and rivers, and thence back to the oceans, from whence it once more evaporates.

Evaporation from all types of surfaces in this cycle involves the utilization of solar energy, and so takes place most readily in equatorial regions. Water vapour is freely distributed by mass movements of air to cooler regions, where it condenses, and then forms large particles which fall under the influence of gravity. Some of the solar energy absorbed during evaporation becomes converted to the kinetic energy of the falling drops or crystals. Incidentally, when water falls on to bare soil, the impact of each drop exerts a considerable disruptive force, breaking the soil crumbs into smaller particles easily carried away by surface run-off, and greatly accelerating water erosion.

2. Effects of Restricted Water Supply on Plants

(a) **General effects.** In spite of the limitations imposed by heredity, the anatomical, morphological and physiological characteristics of a plant are often a close expression of its environment, and are especially influenced by the water factor. Those parts of a plant which show prominent structural variations in response to the prevailing conditions of water balance, are termed **xeroplastic**.

When two sets of seedlings of ordinary plants such as tomatoes are raised under widely different conditions of moisture stress, the effects of unfavourable water balance are very soon apparent. This may be done by controlling the humidity, and hence the transpiration rate, or by carefully controlling the water supply, or by a combination of both methods. Many of the differences which appear between the two sets of plants result from the fact, previously noted in this book, that water is required for the enlargement of newly-formed cells. Thus, both the stems and leaves of the plants raised under the more exacting circumstances are stunted. There seems to be little effect upon cell division, so that the total number of cells is much the same in each case. Since the cells are smaller, the stomata are also reduced in size, and appear closer together. Also, the intercellular spaces in the mesophyll are less extensive. The deposition of cell wall materials appears to be enhanced, a feature which is doubtless correlated with the reduced growth rate, so that cell walls, and also the cuticle, are much thicker. The amount of lignification is strikingly increased, making the plant much tougher, and less flexible. The additional supporting tissue provided by the extra lignification is an important factor in increasing the resistance of these plants to the harmful effects of desiccation (see p. 132). An important feature which undoubtedly favours moisture retention is the increased osmotic potential of the cell contents of the plants grown under the less favourable conditions (see p. 129). Also, it is noteworthy that the depth of the root system may increase in response to an unfavourable water balance, a feature which favours increased water absorption. Further reference to all these factors is made during the course of this chapter.

Different parts of a plant may be subjected to marked differences in moisture stress, and this factor is partly responsible for the structural variations often present between, for example, those leaves which have developed mainly in bright sunlight, and those shaded for most of the time. Thus, sun-leaves, as in the case noted above, have smaller cells, smaller stomata and vein-islets, thicker cells walls and cuticle, and a less extensive internal atmosphere, than shade leaves. Similar differences have been noted between equally illuminated leaves growing at different levels on the same tree, which may be correlated with their relative distances from the water supply. In addition, leaves growing at the higher levels have, in some cases, been found to possess higher osmotic potentials than those lower down (see p. 94).

(b) **Wilting.** In its most common usage, the term 'wilting' refers to the bending or drooping of parts of plants as a result of loss of turgor. In a wider, physiological sense, however, the term can be applied whenever a water deficit is incurred by a plant organ, irrespective of whether or not it produces visible effects. A water deficit is incurred whenever absorption proceeds more slowly than transpiration. The chief causes of inadequate absorption are listed together below. Most of them are treated separately in other sections of this book.

1 The resistance offered by plant tissues to the passage of water (see p. 92).
2 Low soil moisture status (see p. 110).
3 Inadequate size and/or form of root system.
4 Low soil temperature (see p. 114).
5 High osmotic potential of soil solution (see p. 115). (Rarely of practical importance.)

Various stages or degrees of physiological wilting are recognized, these being summarized in Table 2.

The degree of water deficit necessary to produce visible effects varies greatly according to the amount of mechanical tissue present. Thus, as indicated in Table 2, visible wilting in ordinary plants is almost entirely confined to leaves and soft stems. It occurs perhaps most readily in the stems and leaves of young seedlings, especially if these have previously been raised rapidly under humid conditions,

Type of Wilting	Frequency	Degree of Turgor Loss	Visible Effects	Duration
Incipient	Probably daily around midday, especially in summer.	Slight, and short-lived.	None.	Short. Recovery takes place when the transpiration rate falls slightly.
Transient	Often, mainly on hot, dry or windy days.	More marked.	Obvious drooping of leaves and perhaps of herbaceous stems.	Short. Recovery takes place when transpiration is reduced, as at night.
Permanent	Occasionally, chiefly during prolonged dry periods.	Very severe.	Marked drooping of leaves and often of herbaceous stems.	Persists until soil moisture is replenished. So little water is available that deficits cannot be restored merely by reducing transpiration.
Irreversible	Only in very prolonged dry periods.	Complete, and permanent.	Very severe drooping of softer parts, followed by withering.	Permanent. Tissues have become so desiccated that virtually no water is absorbed even if supplied. Death follows.

Table 2. States of physiological wilting

Where the amount of mechanical tissue is adequate by itself to carry out support as in the case of woody stems, visible wilting does not take place. In certain types of plants, the assimilating tissue is so strongly lignified that very large water deficits may exist even here without any outward signs being shown. Such plants usually belong to the category of xerophytes, which are discussed in Section 5(a) of the present chapter.

It should be realized that, in nature, even prolonged withdrawal of water from plant cells, well beyond the point at which turgor is lost, does not result in plasmolysis, as it does in the laboratory when cells are bathed in a hypertonic liquid medium (p. 28). In these experiments, the cell wall is saturated with the plasmolyticum, and water is abstracted only from the protoplast and vacuole. Thus the protoplast shrinks away from the wall, and the plasmolyticum enters the space between them. Under natural conditions in, for example, a drying leaf, water is withdrawn from all parts of a cell, as well as from the surrounding tissues. In any case there is no liquid available to enter between the protoplast and cell wall, which tend to adhere closely, so that the whole cell, including the wall, contracts. If the cells are large and thin-walled, they may collapse at an early stage, but if the walls are more robust, collapse is less likely to occur, and the walls are merely drawn inwards, assuming a slightly concave form. Also, the smaller the cells, the more strongly do they resist collapse for a given thickness of wall. Since cell walls are elastic, they tend to regain their original undistorted state, which means that they impose an additional tension upon the cell contents. This constitutes a negative wall pressure, now acting *with* the osmotic potential of the concentrated vacuolar sap in determining the overall D.P.D. of the cell. (D.P.D. = O.P. − − W.P.) It is easy to see from this that, *provided the cells do not collapse*, very large D.P.D.s may be exerted by the tissues of wilted plants, placing the xylem contents under correspondingly severe strains. The tensions increase as drying progresses, and eventually some or all of the water columns rupture, and/or the cells of the leaf mesophyll and of other tissues collapse, losing their structural organization, and being incapable of recovery. Also, the protoplasm may be torn by such severe mechanical strains that its structural basis is completely disrupted.[1] The tissues then wither, and abscission of leaves takes place. A point is reached where the plant will no longer absorb water at an adequate rate for survival, even if it becomes available in the soil. This is, of course, due to the death of many of the cells, particularly root hairs, together with the lack of sufficient intact water columns.

3. Soil Moisture

(a) **General.** The usefulness of soil to plants lies largely in the fact that it retains for a time much of the water which reaches it by way of precipitation or irrigation, and so acts as a reservoir upon which the vegetation can draw.

During a period of moderate rainfall or irrigation, a layer of soil near to the surface becomes temporarily saturated, most of the pore spaces becoming water-filled. In many soils, such spaces account for about half the total soil volume. Much of this water cannot be retained, and immediately begins to percolate into lower layers, chiefly under the influence of gravity, but partly also by capillarity. When, after some hours, percolation has practically ceased, free water still remains in the form of quite extensive films around the particles, filling a good many of the pore spaces. The soil water level is now said to be at **field capacity**, which is defined as **the maximum amount of**

---

[1] It seems that these strains, rather than the mere fact of desiccation, bring about the death of protoplasm. This is supported by the observation that if tissues are allowed to dry very slowly under carefully controlled laboratory conditions, they will in many cases regain their former state so long as they are allowed to imbibe water again only very slowly.

water which a well-drained soil can retain without significant losses owing to percolation under gravitational or capillary forces. At field capacity, water can be withdrawn by a force of as little as about half an atmosphere, so that at this moisture level, water is readily available to plants. Somewhat surprisingly, however, this force is sufficient to prevent much movement into drier layers, so that there is frequently a sharp boundary between a region of soil at field capacity, and a zone of much drier soil below. Thus the effect of a period of rainfall or irrigation is to bring a layer of soil to field capacity, the depth of the layer depending upon the amount of water supplied. If a subsequent application of water follows reasonably quickly, the thickness of the layer of soil at field capacity is increased, since the additional water soon percolates through the layer previously raised to this level. If sufficient water is applied, some reaches the water table, so that it rises nearer to the surface. After a period of such prolonged or heavy rainfall, the moisture content of the soil just above the water table may be raised somewhat above field capacity by capillary action, but the extent to which the water table affects the moisture status in this way is surprisingly small. Even in a clay soil there is no significant effect on soil more than about ten feet above the table. This is because the pore spaces cannot be considered as simple capillaries, but more as an irregular aggregation of minute compartments, whose nature will depend upon the size, shape and degree of compactness of the particles. Water rises less far in these spaces than in straight tubes, and, just as important, the *rate* of rise is very slow.

In low-lying ground, or in areas overlying impervious strata, the water table often approaches or breaks through the surface. This means that the pore spaces in the region of soil exploited by plant roots are waterlogged. If this situation is prolonged, growth is adversely affected. The roots become oxygen-starved, the soil becomes acidic and anaerobic micro-organisms flourish. In most areas, the level of the water table constantly fluctuates, especially seasonally, as determined by the current levels of precipitation and evapotranspiration.

(b) The availability of soil moisture to plants. Soils retain water largely in the form of surface films around the particles, many of the pore spaces being water-filled. The force with which water is retained in a pore space is inversely proportional to the radius of the pore, so that as the total water content is progressively reduced by evapotranspiration, the largest pores empty first, and increasingly greater forces are required to remove more moisture. Since the forces which plants can bring to bear in absorbing water are very limited, soil water is not equally available to them, especially at the *rate* at which it may be required.

In a saturated or waterlogged layer of soil, as might be found during or immediately after a period of rainfall, water is very easily removed, the magnitude of the force required being determined chiefly by the extremely low D.P.D. of the soil solution, due to the presence of traces of solutes. As field capacity is approached, forces of attraction between the water and particles come into play, amounting, at this stage, to perhaps half an atmosphere. Plants can easily draw on this rather weakly held water. As the soil around the roots becomes progressively drier, however, the films of moisture become greatly reduced in thickness, so that the remaining water in this region becomes increasingly represented by that which is held by very large surface forces in the smallest pore spaces, and by forces of imbibition and hydration within the actual structure of the finer, colloidal, soil particles. Away from the root region, the soil may be a good deal more moist, but owing to the extreme narrowness of the surface films in the soil near the root, capillary movement from these more moist regions is far too slow to be of any appreciable benefit if transpiration is at all rapid. It is here that the constantly extending root systems of many plants become important, in tapping new sources of moisture; root hydrotropism may also be of some significance here. In addition, the *form* of the root system is important, for a richly branched fibrous system will dehydrate a given soil mass far more effectively than a poorly branched one.

That tremendously greater forces are required to remove water from a soil at, say, permanent wilting percentage than at field capacity is shown by the data presented in Fig. 30 which relates the soil moisture tension of a typical loam to the actual moisture content. In addition, and perhaps more important, the conductivity of a soil decreases much more rapidly even than the moisture tension increases, as dehydration proceeds. Before long, plants pass into a state of permanent wilting, this being the point at which plants do not recover unless the soil is watered. In less severe types of wilting, recovery can be brought about merely by reducing the transpiration rate (see p. 108). When permanent wilting occurs, the soil moisture films around the root are so attenuated that even if much more water is present in adjoining areas it is not conducted to the root by capillarity at anything like the required rate, and growth ceases. The soil moisture tension at this point is about 15 atmospheres, but in order to maintain a sufficient rate of water uptake, a D.P.D. greatly in excess of this would have to be exerted by the root system. In other words, by the time the soil moisture tension has risen to about 15 atmospheres, an impossibly steep D.P. gradient would have to exist between the root and the soil moisture in order to bring about an adequate flow of water, not principally because of the increased moisture tension, but chiefly because of the extremely low conductivity of the soil at these

The soil water remaining at the permanent wilting percentage is often referred to as **unavailable water**, but as was pointed out earlier, very large D.P.D.s may develop in wilted plants, so that water may still be abstracted from even a very dry soil by plants in this condition, though at far too slow a rate to permit growth. Thus the term 'unavailable water' is not a strictly accurate one. It will, however, be realized that the maximum amount of water *usefully* available to plants which a soil can store is represented by the difference between the amount held at field capacity (in the form of quite extensive films around soil particles, filling a good many pore spaces) and that held at the permanent wilting point (in the form of very thin films, which fill only the smallest pore spaces). In either case, water is held also by imbibitional and other forces, chiefly in any colloidal matter which may be present. A clay soil, with its preponderance of finely divided colloidal particles, giving a large surface area for water films, as well as a high imbibitional capacity, retains much more water, both at field capacity and at permanent wilting point, than a sandy one, whose non-colloidal particles possess a much smaller total surface area. The data presented in Table 3 illustrate the point that the amounts of both usefully available and 'unavailable' water are much greater in clay soils than in lighter ones.

Soil Type	Approximate Percentage of Water		
	At Field Capacity	At Permanent Wilting Point	Usefully Available to Plants
Clay	28	13	15
Loam	18	8	10
Sandy loam	11	3	8
Fine sand	4	1	3

Table 3. Some soil moisture characteristics[1]

In spite of the usefulness of the permanent wilting percentage as an index of soil moisture characteristics, experimentally obtained values for this quantity should be interpreted with some caution. In the laboratory, the plants are allowed to transpire until they do not recover when placed in a humid atmosphere, and the percentage of moisture remaining in the soil is then determined. The values obtained are apt to vary, according to the actual rate of transpiration that has taken place. With rapid water loss, the value is higher than when a slow rate of transpiration only is permitted. In the former case, due to the sluggishness of capillary movement, the region of soil immediately

[1] Data mainly from Veihmeyer, Amer. Geophys. Union Trans., 612–619 (1938).

around the roots is rapidly depleted of water before much has travelled from other regions. Thus the total soil mass is less thoroughly dried than if water is abstracted slowly. A further complication is that some parts of a plant, usually the lower, most mature leaves, may wilt in advance of younger regions, so making the determination of the permanent wilting point less precise. Also, the form of the root system is an important feature, for, as previously mentioned, plants such as grasses, with a finely divided root system, will lower the soil water content much more effectively than other plants with less richly branched systems, again because of the slowness of capillary movement. Finally, the temperature must be kept under strict control, for this has a marked effect upon the rate of water absorption by roots. Indeed, wilting may readily be induced in many plants by lowering the soil temperature, even if plenty of water is available. This seems to be due to the increased viscosity of water, and the decreased permeability of cytoplasm at lower temperatures, thus greatly increasing the roots' resistance to flow. Also, any active component of water uptake (see p. 100) will be depressed, due to decreased respiration. Over a longer period, there may be an effect due to the decreased formation of new roots. It is interesting to note that the susceptibility of water absorption by plants to low temperatures is often correlated with the temperature range of their native habitat. Species native to northern latitudes are thus least affected, whilst tropical ones are much more sensitive.

In making direct laboratory determinations of the permanent wilting percentage, the plants are grown in non-porous pots placed in a constant temperature water bath. Grass and sunflower plants are usually grown together in the soil under investigation, the former to dry out the soil uniformly, and the latter serving as indicator plant, since it shows wilting very plainly. Bell jars are placed over the wilted plants at intervals, to reduce transpiration. If recovery does not take place under these conditions, permanent wilting is assumed, and the soil moisture content is determined experimentally.

It has been noted above that, over the range of soil moisture between field capacity and permanent wilting percentage, the moisture-retaining forces increase from less than half an atmosphere to about 15 atmospheres (Fig. 30). As the soil moisture content decreases over this range, water uptake by plants proceeds with increasing difficulty. Thus, it has been shown, for example, that the growth of bean plants falls by as much as 50 per cent from the optimum when the D.P.D. of the soil is only reduced to 3 or 4 atmospheres. This increase in the difficulty with which water is absorbed over the range between field capacity and permanent wilting percentage, is not as great as it might be, however. This is because, as the soil dries, the osmotic potential of the root cells increases somewhat, so that the D.P.D. of the cells tends to reflect, over this narrow range, the soil-moisture-retaining forces. This is no longer the case at the lower soil moisture levels, for, as already pointed out, an impossibly high D.P.D. would be necessary in the root cells to maintain an adequate rate of uptake.

Experiments have been carried out in which the rates of evaporation from various types of gradually drying soils, when placed over sulphuric acid, were measured.[1] It was found that, in each case, evaporation proceeded rapidly and uniformly until a certain point was reached, when the rate was suddenly and dramatically reduced (Fig. 31). The percentage of water remaining in the soil at this point was always found to approximate to the permanent wilting percentage, as determined directly. The importance of this is that it indicates some sudden, abrupt change in soil moisture characteristics when the permanent wilting percentage is reached, in which the D.P.D. of the soil water increases very sharply. Thus, as already stated, the point at which permanent wilting takes place is largely independent of the forces which can be exerted by a plant in order to absorb water.

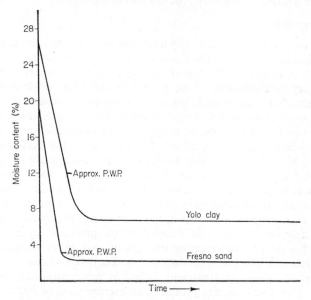

FIG. 31. Evaporation from two different soils placed over 44 per cent H_2SO_4 at about 50 per cent R.H. (altered from Veihmeyer and Hendrickson: see text).

Another factor in plant soil water relations is the osmotic potential of the soil solution. This only becomes of practical importance in

[1] Veihmeyer & Hendrickson. Soil Sci. **80**, No. 1, 61–67 (1955).

special situations, such as when crops are grown in saline soils, or when gross excess of artificial fertilizer has been used in greenhouse cultivation. Up to a few atmospheres, increases in the O.P. of the soil solution are paralleled by increments in that of the root cells. After a certain point, however, growth soon ceases. Halophytes, a specialized group of succulent plants which grow in salt marshes and similar saline situations, however, take up very large amounts of salt from the environment, raising the O.P. of the cells sometimes to over 150 atmospheres. This enables water absorption from the very concentrated solution bathing their roots. Some non-succulent xerophytes growing in arid regions may develop osmotic potentials far exceeding those of ordinary plants. This may be a response to the osmotic potential of the soil solution sometimes encountered in these regions, due to the fact that the unleached solutes produce quite a concentrated solution in the small amount of water present. In such dry soils, however, high D.P.D. of the soil solution is probably of much less significance in preventing water uptake than the enormous moisture-retaining forces developed by the soil particles themselves.

4. Irrigation

The term 'irrigation' is generally used to denote the artificial watering of crops. Many areas of the Earth's land surface will not support the growth of economically important crops simply because of the inadequacy or irregularity of the natural precipitation. In these areas, crop-growing is only made possible by the extensive and scientific application of additional water. In other, less extreme, cases, some crops can be grown without irrigation, but yields are found to be spectacularly increased by its use. For example, in the fruit-growing regions of California, where 85 per cent of all crops are irrigated, there is little or no rainfall during the growing season, and it has been found, as a result of extensive long-term field trials[1] on many types of fruit crops, that unirrigated orchards produce smaller, poorer-quality fruits than irrigated ones. Also, fewer fruits are produced, and the trees may be stunted. The detailed effects produced by moisture deficiency depend, however, on the type of fruit. In one experiment, two plots which had been producing almost equal quantities of prunes were given differential treatment. Irrigation was continued as before in one plot, and each tree produced an average yield of 290 lb, 21.6 per cent of the fruits being graded as large-sized. In the other plot, irrigation was abandoned. The average yield fell to 172 lb, only 2.7 per cent of the fruits being large-sized, so that their market value was greatly reduced.

With the magnitude of the world food problem constantly increasing, irrigation practices are assuming more and more im-

[1] Veihmeyer & Hendrickson. Univ. Calif. Agr. Exp. Sta. Circular 486 (1960).

portance. A vast amount of expenditure is being poured into the introduction of suitable projects for the harnessing of rivers, streams and other natural resources to this end. Much research is also going on into the possibility of using purified sea water, the principal problem being that of cheap desalination on a large scale. In the seventeen Western States of America, nearly all the rice, sugar, vegetable and fruit crops are irrigated, as well as two-fifths of the hay and forage production, a third of the cotton, and a tenth of the grain crops.

In carrying out irrigation, it is certainly not satisfactory to apply water indiscriminately, for excessive or careless watering can be just as harmful as an inadequate supply. For example, if the soil is water-logged, the roots may become oxygen-starved and their growth seriously impaired. Also, extensive leaching can occur, resulting in the loss of essential solutes, although in some very saline soils leaching may be encouraged in an attempt to reduce the excessively high solute content. A further danger is that if the actual irrigation channels are not sited correctly, with due regard to the slope of the land, serious erosion may take place. Furthermore, the supply of water may be costly, so that by avoiding waste, much unnecessary expenditure is avoided. From the growers' point of view, a proper balance must be maintained between the cost of irrigation and the economic value of the benefit likely to be achieved.

Researches, again in the U.S.A.,[1] have shown that for crops such as apples, pears, peaches, grapes and walnuts, it is more satisfactory to wait until the soil reservoir is nearly empty (i.e. until the permanent wilting percentage is almost reached) before replenishing it, than to keep the soil moisture level at a permanently high level by frequent irrigation. If the latter course is followed, the extra benefit, if any, is far outweighed by the additional costs incurred. It was found that, for fruit trees, if the soil moisture level is allowed to remain at the permanent wilting percentage whilst fruit enlargement is proceeding, their growth is greatly impaired and the effect is irreversible, even if the soil is subsequently watered. So long as the permanent wilting percentage is not reached, however, no adverse effects on fruit size are said to appear. It is also claimed that, outside the growing period, the soil moisture level may be maintained at the permanent wilting percentage for periods of up to a fortnight without serious harm. It is important, especially in the main growing period, that the grower should be able to anticipate the onset of permanent wilting, so that irrigation may be initiated in good time. Here, some of the broad-leaved weeds serve a useful function as indicator plants, since wilting is more obvious in these than in the trees themselves, and it occurs sooner, since their roots exploit the shallower, drier layers of the soil.

[1] Veihmeyer & Hendrickson. Univ. Calif. Agr. Exp. Sta. Circular 486 (1960).

A major difficulty in calculating irrigation need is the fact that the responses of different crops to a given degree of water deficit vary widely, and from area to area. Whilst in certain cases, such as those in the U.S.A. mentioned above, growth may be relatively unimpaired by soil moisture levels down to the permanent wilting percentage, this is certainly not a general rule. Often, yields appear to be seriously reduced by only small water deficits. The root systems of such crops as lettuces and tomatoes, for example, are much more shallow, mainly in the drier layers of soil, but, on the other hand, the roots are constantly extending into new regions as development proceeds. The soil moisture requirements of such plants are likely to differ considerably from those of orchard trees and other perennials.

In this country, the scientific application of irrigation procedures is in its infancy, although much research is now being done. It seems that irrigation is the most hopeful means of increasing yields now that the benefits of practices such as manuring and the application of weed killers have been almost fully exploited. At present, the crops most frequently irrigated, usually by means of sprinkler systems, are the annual market garden crops of the lettuce and tomato type. Here, it has been found that, as in the case of the fruit trees noted above, the most serious effects of restricted soil moisture appear in the fruit enlargement phase (where applicable). But whereas some workers claim that growth is little affected so long as the permanent wilting point is not reached, so advocating heavy but less frequent watering as described above, others claim that more benefit is obtained if the same quantity of water is administered in more frequent, lighter, applications, so keeping the upper layers of soil well above the permanent wilting percentage throughout.[1] This controversy continues, and it is clear that much remains to be elucidated concerning the water requirements of different crops before the best and most economical use can be made of irrigation practices. The answers to the many problems can only come from extensive field trials of each crop under each individual set of circumstances.

In assessing irrigation need in this country, use has been made of a quantity known as **potential transpiration**. This is defined as the amount of transpiration taking place from a crop completely covering the ground, of about the same colour as grass, under conditions where the water supply is non-limiting. The quantity is thought not to vary significantly between any of the crops commonly grown in this country, since it depends principally on the weather conditions, and very little on the plant. Its value can be calculated from readily recordable meteorological data, and predicted with reasonable accuracy for any period of the year. Here, the basic assumption is made that

[1] 'Plants and their water supplies', J. P. Hudson. Endeavour XVI, No. 62 (1957).

whenever the soil moisture level falls sufficiently to reduce transpiration growth is impaired. The aim is to apply the amount of water,
over and above the rainfall, which is required to keep actual transpiration at the level of potential transpiration. Irrigation is, of
course, only needed in the summer months, and the simplest way to
calculate the need would be to subtract the summer rainfall from the
calculated potential transpiration and to apply the difference by way
of irrigation. However, at the end of, say, April, the soil is likely to be
at field capacity, and if this simple procedure were to be adopted, this
high level of soil moisture would be maintained throughout the
summer. Experiments have indicated that this is not necessary, and it
appears that a soil moisture deficit below field capacity of the
equivalent of about 3″ of rainfall can be tolerated by many plants
without reducing transpiration or growth. This value is known as the
root constant. For shallow-rooted seedlings, the root constant is
probably less than 3″, whilst for deep-rooted trees, it may be as much
as 10″. Thus, assuming the soil to be at field capacity to begin with, the
procedure for calculating the irrigation need for a given area and crop
would be as follows:

1 Calculate the potential transpiration for the period and area
   (e.g. 15″).
2 Subtract an allowance for the crop root constant (e.g. 3″).
3 Subtract rainfall (e.g. 7″).
∴ Irrigation need for season = (15 − 3) − 7 = 5″.

The grower must then decide upon how the application of this total
amount of water should be spread over the season. Again, meteorological data can give guidance on this point. Up-to-date monthly
average figures for both potential transpiration and for rainfall
relating to particular regions are available to growers through the
Meteorological Office.

Two advantages accrue from allowing the soil moisture level to be
depleted to the equivalent of, say, 3″ below field capacity. Firstly,
expenditure on unnecessary irrigation is avoided, since growth is not
impaired by such a small deficit, and secondly some margin is allowed
for periods of heavy, unexpected rainfall, which might otherwise raise
the soil moisture level well above field capacity for a period, to the
possible detriment of the crop due to waterlogging.

The Meteorological Office have prepared a general picture of the
likely irrigation need for England and Wales in map form.[1] In Map I
is shown the average potential transpiration for the months April-
September, whilst Map II gives the average rainfall for the same
period. Map III provides an indication of the general need for

[1] 'The Calculation of Irrigation Need', Min. Agr., Fisheries & Food Tech.
Bull. No. 4, H.M.S.O.

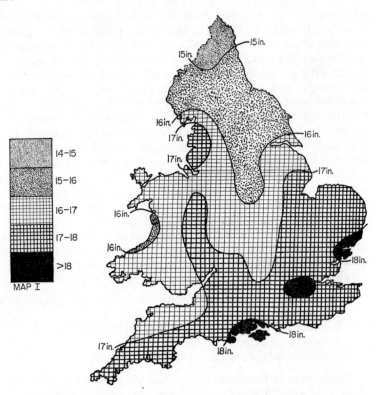

░░	14–15
▒▒	15–16
▦	16–17
▦▦	17–18
■	>18

MAP I

MAP I. Average Summer potential transpiration (April–September) for period 1930–1949 (in inches). Reproduced by permission of the Controller H.M.S.O.

irrigation, allowing for a net depletion of soil water over the period equivalent to about 3″ of rainfall, as explained above. It will be seen that, south-east of a line running approximately from the mouth of the Humber to the Bristol Channel, crops would benefit from some irrigation at least five years in ten, increasing to a frequency of over nine years in ten in certain areas of Suffolk, Essex, Kent, Sussex and the London area. It should be noted that, since this map is a seasonal analysis, it conceals those years which contain a significant, but limited, dry period, during which irrigation might be needed. It must also be emphasized that only a general picture is provided, and that the requirements of particular crops vary considerably. The frequencies shown are likely to be under-estimates in the case of crops with low root constants, and over-estimates for plants, mainly very deep-rooted perennials, with high root constants.

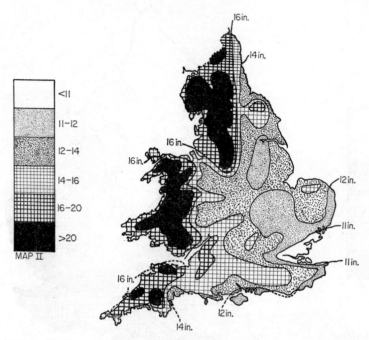

MAP II. Average Summer rainfall (April–September) for period 1916–1950 (in inches). Reproduced by permission of the Controller H.M.S.O.

Recent work on potato crops[1] has shown, for example, that for maximum yield, a soil moisture deficit of only $\frac{1}{2}''$ is desirable during the period when the tubers are in their rapid expansion phase. In the case of new potatoes, this period covers May and June; in the case of maincrop varieties, July and August. In order to meet this requirement, it is considered that, for nearly the whole of England, including the areas generally regarded as 'wet' such as the north-west and west, irrigation during the two critical months would be beneficial in *at least* eight years in every ten. The average amount needed is about $2''$, and whilst in many years much less than $2''$ need be applied, in the driest years at least double this amount would be beneficial.

An interesting, though perhaps expensive, alternative to irrigation which could have commercial possibilities in special regions has recently been introduced in the U.S.A. In this scheme, the soil is ridged to a height of a few inches, and the ridges covered with black polythene sheeting. The crop is grown in the furrows, and receives the moisture

[1] Frequency of Irr. Need for Potato Crops'. Smith & Meads. N.A.A.S. Quart. Rev. No. 54, H.M.S.O. (1961).

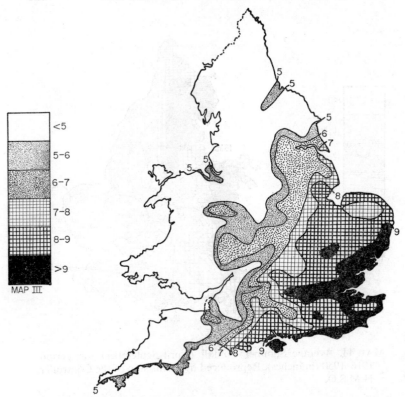

MAP III. General Frequency of Irrigation need (years in ten).
Reproduced by permission of the Controller H.M.S.O.

which drains from the ridges. The sheeting thus has a dual purpose – it reduces evaporation from the soil, and concentrates the precipitation on to the cropped area.

On a small scale, evaporation from soil may be reduced by applying a generous layer of vegetable matter, such as dead leaves, over the surface. This practice is termed **mulching**. Frequent hoeing also helps to reduce evaporation, by filling in any surface cracks which may appear during drying, particularly in the case of heavy soils. It also helps by removing competition by weeds for available moisture.

Mention has been made elsewhere in this book of the harmful effects on plants which can result from too moist a soil. Quite apart from these effects on the plants themselves, the mechanical operations associated with land cultivation may be rendered difficult, or even impossible because of excessive soil water. Removal of excess gravitational water is just as important in some areas as is irrigation in others. Many millions of acres of previously quite unsuitable land have been brought into useful production as the result of the application of suitable drainage projects, and in countless other instances, previously poor yields have been spectacularly increased. Thus, although drainage techniques may involve fairly heavy capital expenditure, both on installation and maintenance, this can be abundantly compensated for by the increased returns which result. Certainly, afar greater land acreage is under drainage at the present time than is subjected to irrigation.

5. Ecological Categories of Plants

In the course of evolution, higher plants have successfully colonized the major part of the Earth's land surface, having become adapted to a tremendous variety of habitats, especially from the standpoint of water relationships. At one end of the scale are those species which exist permanently submerged in water, whilst at the other are those inhabiting regions of extreme dryness. Thus angiosperms display an exceedingly wide range of structural and physiological characteristics by which they are enabled to survive under such widely differing conditions of water balance.

Attempts have been made to distinguish several ecological categories of plants, the three most familiar of which are given the names **xerophytes**, **mesophytes** and **hydrophytes**. Unfortunately, as with any attempted ecological classification, there is no obvious quantitative basis upon which these groups may be delimited, and they are generally (though not satisfactorily) defined in a very broad, relative sense. Xerophytes are those plants which seem best fitted to survive conditions of unfavourable water balance, and hydrophytes are those least able to do so. Mesophytes occupy an intermediate position. Since it is such an ill-defined classification, the terms 'xerophyte' and 'hydrophyte' can only be satisfactorily illustrated by reference to extreme examples of each type. The habitats of the most strikingly xerophytic plants are characterized by prolonged periods of extreme dryness, whilst the most extreme hydrophytes grow completely and permanently submerged in water. In between these, there exists the whole spectrum of intermediate forms, many of which might, for example, be relatively xerophytic in the context of some habitats, and yet in relation to the whole range of plants would be considered to be mesophytes. Xerophytes and hydrophytes are represented by species from the whole range of families, so that there is, in each ecological grouping, much phylogenetic diversity. The members of each category have, however, tended to evolve along similar lines in response to environmental factors, so that quite unrelated forms have often come to resemble one another superficially. This is exemplified by the cactoid appearance of many desert plants from such widely separated families as the

Cactaceae (e.g. *Opuntia* spp), *Euphorbiaceae* (*Euphorbia* spp) and *Compositae* (*Kleinia* spp), and by the uniform appearance of the sclerophyllous flora of the Australian deserts.

Some of the more important morphological, anatomical and physiological characteristics associated with xerophytes and hydrophytes will now be reviewed briefly. It will be realized that no single species of xerophyte or hydrophyte will display all these characteristics, but rather a selection of them.

(a) Xerophytes. Most arid regions experience at least one rainy period during the year, and although such periods are relatively brief, they are often sufficient to allow a wide range of ephemeral plants to complete their life cycle from seed before the most severe drought sets in. The unfavourable period is then survived in the form of the next crop of seeds. Such plants are one of the most characteristic features of the semi-deserts of the U.S.A. Since, in such cases, the plant body does not endure the driest conditions, they may be termed 'drought evaders', and are sometimes excluded from the xerophyte category. However, many of these plants flourish only in these semi-arid zones, and since also the conditions will not support the growth of ordinary ephemerals or annuals, this exclusion seems to be to some extent unjustified.

Broadly speaking, the ways in which those xerophytes which maintain their vegetative organization throughout the entire season are adapted to survive conditions of restricted water supply have two main effects. Firstly, the risk of tissue desiccation is reduced, and secondly, it seems that in most cases the plants can withstand and recover from far greater degrees of tissue desiccation, if and when it occurs, than ordinary plants.

(i) *Transpiration checks.* Experiments have shown that so long as sufficient water is available to them, and provided that the evaporating power of the atmosphere is not excessive, most xerophytes transpire at rates per unit area of leaf which often exceed those of mesophytes.

On p. 106 it was noted that if a given mesophytic species is grown slowly, under conditions of unfavourable water balance, one of the most marked effects is a reduction in cell size, as compared with controls raised under more normal conditions. Thus it is not surprising that small cell size is also one of the most characteristic features of xerophytes, although in this case it is usually a genetically fixed feature, and not a direct response to environment during the life of one set of plants. Reduced cell size is probably the principal reason for the surprisingly high transpiration rates shown by xerophytes under the circumstances noted above, since it means that there are many more stomata and veinlets per unit area of leaf.

In spite of this, xerophytes display important features by reason of which transpiration rates are, under certain circumstances, very much lower than those of ordinary plants. The chief such circumstances are when, for any reason, a water deficit is incurred so that a state of permanent wilting is approached, or merely when the evaporating power of the air rises to a high level. In other words, xerophytes transpire much less rapidly than mesophytes under those external conditions which favour high transpiration rates, or, in addition, whenever a severe water deficit is incurred, usually as a result of poor soil moisture status. Such circumstances predominate in the native habitats of xerophytes, and since restriction of transpiration involves reduced photosynthesis it might be thought that this might seriously impair growth. This is probably not the case, however, since although xerophytes are, in fact, slow-growing plants, this is primarily due to the lack of growth water, and not to the slowness of synthesis.

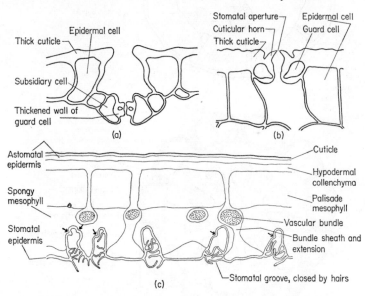

FIG. 32. Stomata of xerophytes. (a) Median vertical section through stoma of *Hakea*, showing depression below leaf surface. (b) Median vertical section through stoma of *Ilex*, showing very thick cuticle. (c) Section through leaf of *Nerium*, showing pits in which groups of stomata are situated. Arrows indicate positions of individual stomata. (Cell contents not shown.)

THICK CUTICLE. A well-developed cuticle is characteristic of many evergreen plants, especially gymnosperms, and of xerophytes in general (Figs. 32, 33, 34). In extreme cases, the cuticle may exceed the thickness of the epidermal layer itself. In such cases, cuticular transpiration is greatly restricted, especially when the cuticle is impregnated with wax. The chief value of this is that when stomatal closure takes place (as, for example, in response to a water deficit) the transpiration rate may become almost nil. The shiny surface which often results from a thick, waxy cuticle is also valuable in reflecting solar radiation, so minimizing the leaf temperature.

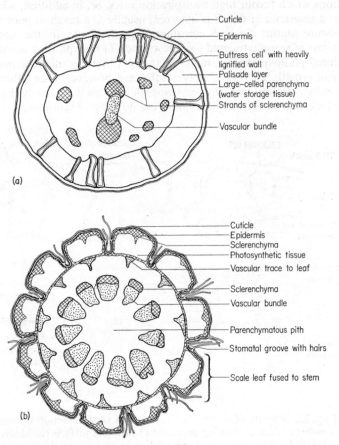

FIG. 33. Structure of (a) leaf of *Hakea* and (b) stem of *Casuarina*, as seen in transverse sections.

DEPRESSION OF STOMATA. A widespread feature of xerophytes, which again is shown to varying degrees, is the depression of stomata below the general level of the plant's surface. Often, depression results simply from the fact that the epidermis, apart from the guard cells, is heavily cuticularised. In other cases, the thickness of the cuticle is accentuated near to stomata and it may even arch over the guard cells so as to form a small cavity between the two, as in *Ilex* (Holly, Fig. 32(b)). Another common situation is for the guard cells to be depressed well below the other epidermal cells, so that an extensive pit, or vestibule, is formed. This is the case in the leaves of *Pinus* and many other gymnosperms, and in plants such as *Hakea*, a native of Australia (Fig. 32(a)). In *Nerium oleander* (Fig. 32(c)) the pits are larger, and take the form of scattered hollows formed by general depressions in the leaf surface, in which groups of stomata occur. In many other plants, stomata are confined to longitudinal grooves as in *Casuarina*, another Australian plant (Fig. 33(b)). Here, the leaves are reduced to scales, and the photosynthetic function is carried out by the stem. This bears longitudinal furrows, at the base of which the stomata are situated.

In all cases, depression of stomata means that the diffusion path of water vapour from the mesophyll to the bulk of the external air is lengthened, so that the diffusion pressure gradient is reduced, cutting down the transpiration rate. This will be of maximum importance under conditions of high wind velocity. Such conditions favour very high transpiration rates, but if a layer of saturated air is maintained in the grooves or pits, this effect is much less pronounced.

ROLLING OR FOLDING OF LEAVES. When a certain degree of water deficit has been incurred, the leaves of certain plants roll or fold in such a way as to protect the stomata, which are usually confined to one surface, the astomatal one being heavily cuticularized. This property is shown by the leaves of *Calluna* (Ling, Fig. 34(b)) and by many grasses such as *Aira* and *Ammophila* (Fig. 34(a)). In the grasses, the stomata are usually afforded the additional protection of being placed in furrows. At the base of these furrows are large, colourless, thin-walled hinge cells. As turgor is lost, these contract and cause the leaf to curl, often tightly, inwards. In other cases (e.g. *Poa*) the leaf merely folds in a V-shaped fashion, bringing the stomatal surfaces towards one another. In either case, only the heavily cuticularized leaf surface is exposed to the atmosphere, and consequently such rolling or folding of leaves is extremely effective in reducing transpiration.

PUBESCENCE. Various degrees of hairiness are met with amongst plants, but dense hairiness is especially associated with the xerophytic habit (Fig. 33, 34). In some cases, as in many plants of mountainous regions exposed to strong winds, a dense felty or mealy layer may be developed over the surface. Where the hairs are sparsely distributed, they probably have no significant effect upon transpiration, but where the covering is dense, or when the hairs appear together with stomata in grooves, they exert a considerable restricting influence by trapping a layer of still, moist air above the guard cells, so reducing the steepness of the diffusion pressure gradient. Again, this feature is of greatest value during windy conditions. A similar result is achieved by another property shown by many plants native to mountainous regions, whereby the leaves grow in close rosette-like formations near to the ground, so that moist air tends to accumulate between them.

Hairs may also be of value in restricting transpiration by reflecting some solar radiation, so keeping down the leaf temperature.

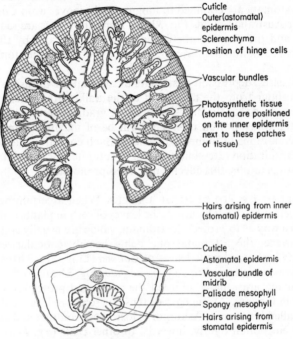

Cuticle
Outer(astomatal) epidermis
Sclerenchyma
Position of hinge cells

Vascular bundles

Photosynthetic tissue
(stomata are positioned
on the inner epidermis
next to these patches
of tissue)

Hairs arising from inner
(stomatal) epidermis

Cuticle
Astomatal epidermis
Vascular bundle of
midrib
Palisade mesophyll
Spongy mesophyll
Hairs arising from
stomatal epidermis

FIG. 34. Structure of leaf of (a) *Ammophila* and (b) *Calluna* as seen in transverse section. Both leaves are shown in a part-closed position.

REDUCTION OF TRANSPIRING SURFACE. Few xerophytes bear the dorsi-ventral type of leaf characteristic of mesophytes. Often, leaves are dispensed with altogether, or reduced to mere scales, the photosynthetic function being transferred to a stem or flattened petiole. In other cases, leaves are produced during rainy periods, only to be shed later. Sometimes, the entire aerial parts may disappear, the plant persisting as a fleshy root or other underground structure.

Those xerophytes which bear persistent foliage frequently have centric leaves, as exemplified by *Hakea* (Fig. 33(a)) and *Pinus*. In such cases, the leaves are somewhat cylindrical in general form, and roughly circular in transverse section. The chief importance of this is that a cylinder exposes a relatively much smaller transpiring area per unit volume than the usual flattened structure. Also, greater structural rigidity is obtained.

VARIATIONS IN LEAF POSITION. In a near horizontal position, leaves absorb solar radiation almost at right angles, and thus receive the maximum amount of illumination and heating effect. In some plants, the position of the leaf blade becomes adjusted so that the sun's rays strike them much more obliquely. If the leaves of the European 'compass plants' (*Lactuca* spp) are exposed to bright sunlight, they become orientated with their edges pointing north-south, and it is thought that the temperature reduction brought about in this way is sufficient to reduce the transpiration rate significantly. In both *Robinia* and *Oxalis*, the leaflets are more or less horizontally placed, unless exposed to bright sunlight for a period when they move to a more nearly vertical position.

THE NATURE OF THE CELL CONTENTS. The vacuolar sap of many xerophytes is a very highly concentrated solution, and frequently large amounts of pentosan mucilages and gums are present. The high osmotic potential of the cell contents may be no more than a response to the high osmotic potential of the soil solution sometimes encountered in arid regions (p. 116) but it is also likely that, in some way not understood, it helps to restrict evaporation from the cell walls (p. 84). Also, the presence of the large amounts of colloidal mucilages almost certainly increases the resistance of the cells to desiccation, for such substances hold water tenaciously.

(ii) *Succulence in xerophytes*. Many desert plants absorb water rapidly during the brief periods of availability, and store it in specialized aqueous tissues for long periods. When the amount of aqueous tissue is great, the plant takes on a fleshy character, and its surface area: volume ratio is very much smaller than that of ordinary plants. In the *Cactaceae*, succulence is usually confined to the stem, and a photosynthetic layer surrounds the central water storage tissue. The leaves are reduced to scales or spines. In the *Crassulaceae*, on the other hand, both stems and leaves are generally succulent as in *Bryophyllum* (Fig. 35). Succulent plants are characterized by extremely low transpiration rates, even when supplied with abundant water, and in this last respect they differ from other xerophytes. This is associated with the presence of an extremely effective cuticle, relatively small surface area, and the large amounts of moisture-retaining mucilages in the cells. As the dry season progresses, the cells shrink, and their walls may become infolded. However, they normally suffer no permanent injury, and recover turgor when water again becomes available. These plants cannot endure tissue desiccation to the same extent as other xerophytes, so that conservation of stored water is all-important.

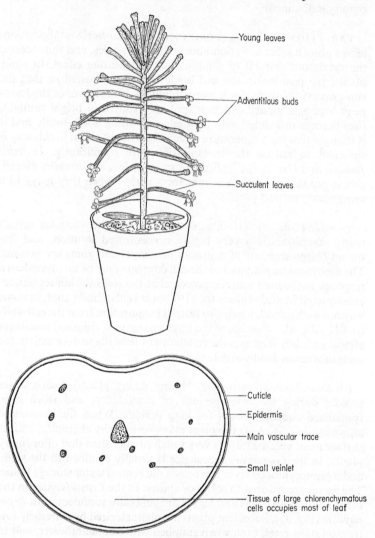

Fig. 35. *Bryophyllum tubiflora*. Lower drawing shows shape of succulent leaves in transverse section.

Succulent plants possess the additional peculiarity of stomatal closure during the daytime, when the evaporating power of the atmosphere is greatest, and opening at night. In this way considerable water conservation is achieved. This is associated with peculiarities in metabolism. During the hours of darkness, when the stomata are open, carbon dioxide is absorbed by a dark-fixation process, and combined with pyruvic acid (an intermediate compound in respiration) to produce organic acids, principally malic acid. In the light, these acids are decomposed to produce carbon dioxide again. Since the stomata are now closed, the gas does not escape, and is used in photosynthesis. The biochemistry of the process has not been fully elucidated, but it is at least clear that photosynthesis is able to continue whilst the stomata are closed. Dark fixation of carbon dioxide is now known to occur in many other plants besides succulents, though to a much smaller extent. (See p. 73.)

The root systems of desert succulents are usually very shallow, but with an extremely wide lateral spread. This enables them to absorb water very efficiently over a large area when the upper layers of soil are moistened, so that even light rains are beneficial. When the soil dries, the roots may disappear, fresh ones being put forth in subsequent rainy spells. Such a shallow type of root system would be impossible for those xerophytes without large water-storage capacities, for the surface layers of soil are the first to dry out during the rainless periods.

Many succulents have striking powers of vegetative propagation. In the *Crassulaceae*, for example, leaves may become detached and lie on the surface of the soil for months during the dry season. When the rains come, adventitious roots are rapidly put forth, and a new plant appears.

(iii) *Extensive root systems.* The underground systems of xerophytes are usually far more extensive, relative to the aerial portions, than in ordinary plants. Thus the minimum transpiring area is exposed, and if the roots are profusely branched, the moisture in a given volume of soil is exploited with greater efficiency (p. 111). Reference has already been made to the extensive root systems possessed by cacti, and to the fact that in other cases the roots may be the only parts to persist through the dry season. Some desert plants bear tap roots which penetrate to great depths. This clearly increases the chances of at least some part of the root system remaining in contact with available water as the soil dries out. But in many desert regions, the nature of the soil itself impedes root penetration. Often, hard rocks occur near to the surface, so that no great depths can be exploited.

(iv) *Resistance to the effects of desiccation.* The ordinary leaf is a delicate photosynthetic organ, relying largely upon cell turgor for support. As was noted earlier, wilting occurs rather readily in such leaves when a water deficit is incurred. When the stage of irreversible wilting is reached, most of the cells collapse, and the protoplasm is subjected to such severe strains that its functional properties are lost.

We have seen that xerophytes possess mechanisms by means of which moisture is conserved, but in spite of this, these plants often endure degrees of tissue desiccation far beyond those tolerated by mesophytes. This resistance appears to be brought about in three main ways.

INCREASED LIGNIFICATION. One of the most characteristic anatomical features of xerophytes is the very large amount of lignified tissue which they contain. (A tendency in this direction, as well as a tendency to increased sturdiness of cell walls in general can also be noted in mesophytes grown under conditions of unfavourable water balance (p. 106).) Owing to the great mechanical strength of lignified tissues, the cells are capable of withstanding the tremendous tensions generated during prolonged wilting, long past the point at which turgor is lost. Since the cells do not collapse, and because the cytoplasm adheres to the cell wall, the protoplast is not damaged nearly so readily as in mesophytes under equivalent conditions. Also, the plants remain upright, showing no outward signs of the tremendous tensions which exist in the hydrostatic system. (The reader should refer to the section on wilting, earlier in this chapter, p. 107.)

In many cases, leaves are absent altogether, are shed in the dry season, or are reduced to scales, with photosynthesis being carried out in the stem. The advantage of this feature lies in the fact that stems are usually much more heavily lignified than leaves, particularly with regard to the presence of more substantial vascular traces and often of

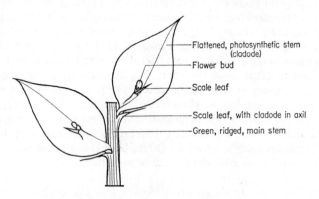

FIG. 36 (a). Morphology of *Ruscus* shoot.

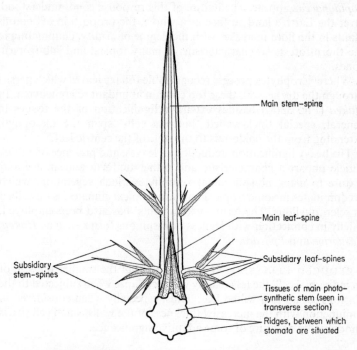

Main stem–spine

Main leaf–spine

Subsidiary leaf–spines

Subsidiary
stem–spines

Tissues of main photo–
synthetic stem (seen in
transverse section)

Ridges, between which
stomata are situated

FIG. 36 (b). Morphology of *Ulex* shoot. A single large stem spine, detached from main stem, and viewed from below.

peripheral sclerenchyma. Sometimes, an assimilating stem assumes a leaf-like external form, as in *Ruscus* (Butcher's Broom Fig. 36(a)). Such a flattened, photosynthetic stem is termed a **cladode**. In this particular case, the true morphological nature of the organ is evidenced by the fact that it is axillary to a scale leaf, and also by the fact that it bears similar scale leaves in one or more of whose axils a flower often appears. In other plants, the leaf lamina is lost, but the petiole assumes a lamina-like form, such a structure being termed a **phyllode** (e.g. *Acacia* spp.). Again, petioles contain much more mechanical tissue than leaves. Monocotyledonous leaves are probably phyllodic in origin. In still other cases, leaves are represented by spines, as in *Berberis* (Barberry). The spines of cacti are also believed to be leaf-like in origin. In *Ulex europaeus* (Gorse Fig. 36(b)), the leaves are spinous, and bear, in their axils, spinous lateral stems, which in turn produce further leaf-spines. Both the leaf-spines and stem-spines are photosynthetic and highly sclerenchymatous. If Gorse seedlings are raised under humid conditions, leaf-spines are no longer produced, and the trifoliate leaves commonly met with in the

Papilionaceae appear. The nature of this response is not understood. Over the Earth's land surface as a whole, the proportion of spinous plants in the flora increases with the degree of aridity, culminating in the thorn-forests so characteristic of many topical and sub-tropical zones.

Where xerophytes possess recognizable foliage leaves which persist through the dry season, these too contain abundant sclerenchyma. In *Hakea* (Fig. 33(a)) besides extensive lignification of the tissues in general, special thick-walled 'buttress cells' span the mesophyll, extending from the epidermis to the stele of the centric leaf.

The heavy lignification, reduction of leaves, and presence of a thick cuticle impart a characteristic and rather uniform appearance and texture to many non-succulent xerophytes. Such vegetation, which predominates in some tropical and sub-tropical climates, is described as sclerophyllous. The term 'switch-plants' has also been employed, chiefly in connection with leafless non-spinous forms such as *Hakea*, *Casuarina* and *Ephedra*.

REDUCED CELL SIZE. It is probable that the smaller the size of an individual cell, the less readily will it collapse when subjected to the tensions set up in a wilted leaf. Thus, especially when considered in conjunction with the increased thickness of the walls, small cell size is undoubtedly a feature of some adaptive significance.

RESISTANCE OF THE PROTOPLASM. It seems that the protoplasmic colloids of xerophytes are much more tolerant of desiccation than those of mesophytes, since the water content of their cells may be reduced far below normal survival levels without apparent harm. The basis for such resistance is not understood, but it seems to be at least partly due to the presence of large amounts of solutes and mucilages within the substance of the protoplasm itself.

Any plant possessing some of the morphological features associated with xerophytes is said to show xeromorphism, or to be **xeromorphic**. However, not all xeromophic plants are xerophytes. The best known example of this is furnished by salt-marsh angiosperms, a group of plants known as **halophytes**. Most halophytes are of a succulent character, examples being *Salicornia* (Glasswort), *Aster tripolium* (Sea Aster) and *Plantago maritima* (Sea Plantain). Unlike desert succulents, halophytes transpire rapidly, and have no difficulty in absorbing all the water they require. The high salt concentration in the environment is matched by a correspondingly high osmotic potential in the cells of these plants, made possible by the extraordinary permeability of the root cells to chlorides, and the great resistance of the protoplasm to salt. The significance of succulence here is not known, but it seems to be a response to the presence of salt in the environment, for the degree of succulence tends to vary with the actual salt concentration met with. Also, succulence can be induced in some ordinary plants by careful, gradual, introduction of salt into the soil solution.

Another well-known example of xeromorphism in a group of plants which do not appear to lack water in their environment is furnished by our native moorland flora, as exemplified by such plants as *Calluna* (Heather) *Vaccinium myrtilis* (Whortleberry) and many species of *Juncus* (Rushes). These are certainly xerophytes when considered in relation to the British flora. One of the early explanations of the apparent paradox of xerophytes growing in this particular type of wet situation was that, although abundant water is present, it is not readily available to the roots because of the presence of organic acids and other toxic substances resulting from the predominantly water-logged nature of the soil, the anaerobic conditions, and the presence of such plants as *Sphagnum* spp. (Bog moss). Also, the fact that oxygen is deficient hinders root development. Thus, although the soil does not lack moisture in a physical sense, it may not be available to the plants. Conservation of water in such 'physiologically dry' situations is just as important as in cases where actual soil moisture is lacking. The whole question of the ecology of moorland plants is, however, very puzzling, and although few now consider the above explanation to be the correct one, a convincing alternative explanation is not forthcoming.

(b) **Hydrophytes.** Whereas the British flora includes none of the most profoundly modified xerophytes, there are many examples of extreme hydrophytes amongst our native plants. Again, the nature of the environment to which these plants are adapted means that there are strong resemblances between species from a wide range of families. Indeed, the degree of uniformity exceeds that shown by xerophytes, especially from the anatomical standpoint.

It is possible to make a broad distinction between three types of habitats in which hydrophytes occur. Near the banks of areas of open water, or in other low-lying situations, the soil is almost permanently very moist, and often waterlogged. In such circumstances, a definite **marsh flora** occurs, characterized by the presence of such plants as *Caltha palustris* (Marsh Marigold), *Mentha aquatica* (Water Mint), *Myosotis palustris* (Water Forget-me-not), *Scrophularia aquatica* (Water Betony), and many species of *Carex* (Sedges) and *Juncus* (Rushes). The chief problem encountered by these plants is the lack of soil oxygen. This is overcome by the spongy nature of the tissues, by means of which oxygen from the aerial parts finds its way to the underground regions. Frequently, this aerating tissue, which is characterized by the presence of a very high proportion of intercellular spaces, is formed instead of cork from a phellogen. In such cases the tissue is described as aerenchyma. There is an abundance of available water, so that marsh plants frequently have flimsy leaves, with a thin cuticle, and show rapid rates of transpiration. Hydathodes are commonly present, by means of which excess water is removed (p. 103).

Between the marsh and the open water there is usually a definite zone of mud, often covered by a shallow layer of water, and occupied by a well-defined **swamp flora**. The majority of the plants growing here are monocotyledonous 'reeds'. The underground portion of these consists of a system of shallow, richly-branched rhizomes, which anchor the plants very effectively. The leaves are tall, vertically-placed structures, which impart a very characteristic appearance to the swamp zone. Examples of monocotyledonous plants frequently present in this zone are *Sparganium ramosum* (Bur-reed) *Typha latifolia* (Great Reedmace) *Glyceria maxima* (Reed grass) and *Phragmites vulgaris* (Reed). Dicotyledonous plants commonly encountered here are *Lythrum salicaria* (Purple Loosestrife) and *Lycopus europaeus* (Gypsywort). The relative extents of the marsh and swamp zones vary a great deal with such factors as the slope of the land, the swiftness of the current and the amount of silt and organic debris in the water.

The third type of habitat is that in which the plants are partially or totally immersed in a permanent body of water. Here, a true **aquatic flora** exists, and the discussion which follows is concerned entirely with this type of vegetation. Although the mere abundance of water is the most important determinant of the type of vegetation occurring under these conditions, the relative frequency with which the various species are encountered is influenced by such additional factors as the type of substrate, pH, mineral content, presence of organic debris, speed of current and temperature, so that quite different species may be expected to be dominant in different localities.

Most of the hydrophytes rooted in the shallower regions are not completely submerged. *Sagittaria sagittifolia* (Arrowhead), for example, raises many of its leaves well into the air, whilst in the case of *Nymphaea alba* (White Water Lily) most of the leaves float at the surface. Those rooted in the deeper zones, such as *Elodea canadensis* (Canadian Pondweed) and *Ranunculus fluitans* (Water Crowfoot) are, on the other hand, totally immersed. Still other aquatic plants such as *Utricularia* spp. (Bladderwort) and *Lemna* spp. (Duckweeds) are not rooted to the bottom, but float at or near the surface.

The more important characteristics of aquatic plants are briefly reviewed below.

(i) *Anatomical features:*

AERATION TISSUE. Perhaps the most important problem encountered by submerged aquatics is that of obtaining an adequate supply of oxygen. The reason for this difficulty is that oxygen is only sparingly soluble in water. Whereas a litre of air contains about 200 cc of the gas, only about 8 cc is present in the same volume of water when saturated with atmospheric oxygen at ordinary temperatures. Such oxygen as is available is competed for by an enormous range of aquatic organisms. Also, the rate of diffusion of the gas in water is far slower than that in air. The supply of carbon dioxide probably presents little difficulty, since it dissolves much more readily, and is produced by the activities of numerous aquatic organisms, especially by bacteria in the mud.

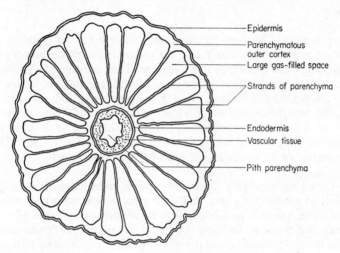

FIG. 37. Structure of stem of *Myriophyllum*, as seen in transverse section.

The shortage of oxygen in the water is met by the development of an extensive internal atmosphere in the submerged stems and leaves. Between the parenchyma cells which compose the bulk of these organs large, normally gas-filled, intercellular spaces exist. In most cases, these spaces are extremely large and are known as **lacunae**. They form an extensive, intercommunicating system throughout the submerged organs in which metabolic gases are stored and are able to circulate (Fig. 37). During periods of reasonably high light intensity, there is a net production of oxygen, which, instead of escaping into the medium, is stored and is available for respiration. Often the lacunae are traversed at intervals by diaphragms composed of very small cells, and perforated by minute intercellular spaces. It is said that water cannot penetrate these spaces, owing to its high surface tension. Thus, although gases are free to pass across, the internal atmosphere is not flooded if water should enter the system at, for example, the site of an injury.

The presence of aerating tissue confers great buoyancy upon the plant, so that the leaves are raised as near as possible to the surface, where there is a higher light intensity, and normally more oxygen, as well as a slightly higher temperature. Since support is carried out in this way, there is a marked absence of strengthening tissue, so that the organs show maximum flexibility. This is important when buffetting by water movements is met with.

Submerged leaves resemble shade leaves (p. 58) in having poorly differentiated palisade tissue. Aerial leaves display the normal leaf structure.

EPIDERMIS. The term 'transpiration' clearly has no meaning in relation to submerged parts, and the cuticle is poorly developed, or even absent altogether on these regions. Thus passage of dissolved gases and mineral salts can take place all over the surface. Stomata, too, are frequently lacking, though in some cases they exist in a reduced, non-functional form. Floating leaves usually bear stomata and cuticle on their upper surface. In the case of *Nymphaea*, the latter is heavily impregnated with wax, so as to be virtually non-wettable. Completely aerial leaves show the normal epidermal structure.

VASCULAR SYSTEMS. Since absorption takes place all over the surface of submerged parts, and since also there is no transpiration from them, xylem is poorly developed in entirely submerged plants. In extreme cases, as in some species of *Potamogeton* (Pondweeds), xylem is entirely lacking, and the elements are represented by lacunae. If floating or aerial leaves are present, however, the reduction of the xylem is less drastic. Phloem is subject to less reduction, for there is still the need for a tissue in which translocation of elaborated organic materials takes place.

The actual distribution of the vascular tissues in hydrophytes is reminiscent of the arrangement found in the roots of land plants, in that there is usually a central core of xylem, surrounded by phloem and an endodermis. This distribution is probably associated with the fact that, like roots, hydrophyte organs have to withstand pulling strains rather than bending. The chief value of this feature, however, probably rests upon the additional flexibility which it allows.

(ii) *Morphological features:*

LEAVES. The depth at which submerged leaves can occur is, of course, limited largely by the light intensity, and beyond this limit no rooted aquatics are to be found.

Submerged leaves are always extremely thin (often translucent) and flexible, and only in occasional cases is there a broad lamina. In the more typical forms, the leaves are either linear (ribbon-shaped) structures, or else the lamina is dissected so as to give it a filamentous character. In either case, the leaves or leaf segments trail parallel with the direction of the current. The value of this is that little resistance is offered to the flow of water, which runs freely between the structures. Also, this arrangement means that none of the leaf cells is far from the external water, upon which the plant is dependent for its metabolic gases. Floating leaves, on the other hand, are usually broad, flat structures, with entire margins. Often, as in *Nymphaea*, the leaves are peltate, the petiole joining the lamina at some point on the lower surface, making a very stable raft-like platform. In this plant, as in many other aquatics, there is no erect stem, and the long flexible petioles arise obliquely from a fleshy rhizome. Within limits, the angle at which the petiole rises through the water can alter so as to adjust the position of the lamina in response to fluctuations in the water level.

Aerial leaves, where they occur, are not subject to any special modifications, and so take a variety of forms. It is therefore possible for an aquatic to bear several types of leaves according to the position of the lamina relative to the water surface. Such plants are said to exhibit **heterophylly**. Examples are afforded by *Ranunculus fluitans* (Water Crowfoot) and *Sagittaria sagittifolia* (Fig. 38). In this case, if the plant is rooted in still water, three types of leaves are produced. If there is a pronounced current, however, only the ribbon-shaped leaves are borne. A similar plasticity of leaf morphology is seen in many other aquatics. The type of leaf produced is influenced by such factors as light intensity, depth of water, and composition of the medium, as well as by speed of current.

STEMS. Where erect stems are borne under the water surface, a degree of etiolation appears. The length of the internodes progressively decreases as the surface is approached, a feature clearly related to the reduced light intensity at the lower levels. This is particularly evident in such plants as *Callitriche* spp. (Water Starwort) and *Potamogeton natans* (Broad-leaved Pondweed).

ROOTS. Roots are not needed for absorption and in general serve only for attachment. They are usually adventitious, and are shorter and much less branched than those of land plants. Root hairs are nearly always absent. Occasionally, trailing roots develop on floating aquatics. In *Lemna* spp. they seem to function as balancing organs.

WINTER-BUD FORMATION. A specialized means of overwintering is adopted by many water plants. This involves the formation of winter buds or **turions**. Here, short lateral shoots, or ends of longer shoots, usually covered with overlapping leaves, become swollen with food reserve, and become detached from the plant, which in many cases dies away in the winter. In the following spring they become active, and produce a new plant. Turions serve both for perennation and vegetative propagation. They are found in such plants as *Elodea*, *Ceratophyllum* (Hornwort), *Utricularia*, and most species of *Potamogeton*, as well as in *Sagittaria*. If a rhizome is present, this frequently persists through the winter, in addition to any turions which may be produced.

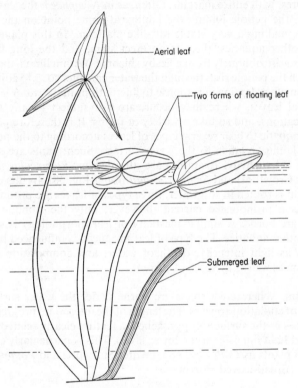

Aerial leaf

Two forms of floating leaf

Submerged leaf

FIG. 38. Sagittaria sagittifolia.

POLLINATION AND SEED DISPERSAL. The great majority of aquatic plants produce flowers above the water surface, these being pollinated by the usual agencies. In a few cases, however, specialized mechanisms for water pollination have been evolved. In *Elodea* and *Vallisneria*, there are separate staminate and pistillate flowers. The staminate ones break away and float, whilst the pistillate flowers elongate until the surface is reached. When pollination has taken place, the flower curls so as to bring the fruit under the water, where it completes development. (In Britain, the staminate plant of *Elodea* is very rare.)

In *Ceratophyllum* and *Zostera* (the Eel-grass of salt marshes) the pollen floats readily (in sea water in the case of *Zostera*) and is transferred directly from the staminate to the pistillate flowers, all of which are submerged. Large quantities of pollen are produced, as the method is very inefficient.

Many of the fruits of aquatic plants resist prolonged submergence in water, and in this respect differ markedly from those of land plants. Often, as in *Nuphar*, they are spongy and buoyant, enabling water dispersal to take place.

REFERENCES

'Soil Moisture', Veihmeyer, 'Encyclopaedia of Plant Physiology' Vol. III, 64–123 (1956).

'Soil moisture in relation to plant growth', Veihmeyer and Hendrickson, Ann. Rev. Plant Phys. 1, 285–304 (1950).

'Plant water deficits and physiological processes', Vaadia, Raney and Hagan Ann. Rev. Plant Phys. 12 (1961).

'The movement of soil water', Childs, Endeavour XXIII, No. 89 (1964).

Bibliography

The Transpiration Stream. H. Dixon. Univ. Lond. Press, (1924).
Water in the Physiology of Plants. Chronica Botanica Co., (1949).
Plant and Soil Water Relationships. Kramer. McGraw-Hill Book C., Inc. (1949).
An Introduction to Plant Physiology. Curtis and Clark. McGraw-Hill Book Co., Inc. (1950).
Plant Physiology. Meyer and Anderson. D. Van Nostrand Co., Inc. (Second Edition) (1952).
Water. U.S.A. Dept. of Agriculture Yearbook for 1955.
Plants and Environment. R. F. Daubenmire. John Wiley and Sons, Inc. (Second Edition) (1959).
The Growth of Plants. G. E. Fogg. Penguin Books, (1963).
A Guide to Subcellular Botany. C. A. Stace. Longmans. (1963).
The Microstructure of Cells. S. W. Hurry. John Murray. (1965).

Useful Periodicals, containing occasional articles on water relations as well as on other aspects of plant physiology are *Endeavour* and *Scientific American.*

The Encyclopaedia of Plant Physiology, published by Springer-Verlag/ Berlin Göttingen-Heidelberg, is an invaluable reference work. Vol. III deals exclusively with water relations, and contains articles on all major aspects by the leading authorities. Many of the articles, however, are in German, and some in French.

The Annual Review of Plant Physiology, published by Annual Reviews, Inc., contains many articles on water relations, in the form of reviews of recent work. There are extensive references to the original papers. Various volumes of this valuable publication are referred to at the end of the relevant chapters of the present work.

List of Practical Directions

Whilst this book is in no way intended to be a complete guide to practical work on Water Relations, adequate directions for performing certain experimental work of an elementary nature are given on the pages indicated below. Other more advanced investigations, for which special apparatus may be required are referred to more briefly in the text.

Demonstration of osmosis *in vitro*   9 – 11
Demonstration of the effects of denaturation of cyto-
    plasmic membranes   25
Demonstrations of osmosis, plasmolysis and recovery
    using plant tissues   30 – 34
Evaluation of the diffusion pressure deficit of plant cells   31 – 33
Evaluation of the osmotic potential of the vacuolar sap   33 – 34
Demonstration of tissue tensions in plant organs   39 – 40
Measurement of degree of stomatal opening   76 – 80
Measurement of transpiration   84 – 87
Demonstration of ability of stem to support a tension   95 – 96
Demonstration of root pressure   99
Demonstration of guttation   103

Index

Acacia, 133
Active uptake, 35, 99–102
Adhesion, 3, 53, 97
Aeration tissue, 135–8
Aerenchyma, 136
Aira, 127
Allium, 70
Ammophila, 127, 128
Annular element, 54, 55
Aspiration, 53
Aster, 134
Auxin, 35–6

Berberis, 133
Berkeley and Hartley, 13
Betula, 83
Birefringence, 20
Bordered pit, 52–4, 56
Brownian movement, 4, 5, 20
Bryophyllum, 129, 130

Cactaceae, 70, 73, 124, 129
Callitriche, 139
Calluna, 127, 128, 135
Caltha, 135
Capillarity, 3, 18, 64, 90, 101, 110, 111
Carex, 135
Casparian strip, 44–5
Casuarina, 126, 127, 134
Cell wall, 17–19, 26
Cellulose, 17, 18–19, 26, 64
Centric leaf, 129
Ceratophyllum, 140, 141
Chloroplast, 17, 23, 24
Chromoplast, 17
Cladode, 133
Cobalt chloride, 77–8, 85
Cohesion, 1–3, 97
Collenchyma, 40, 58
Colloid, 4–6, 8, 21
Colocasia, 103

Concentration gradient, 7
Cortex, 44
Crassulaceae, 70, 73, 129, 131
Cryoscopic method, 33
Cucurbitaceae, 95
Cuticle, 59–60, 61, 62, 75
Cuticle of xerophyte, 125–6, 127
Cutin, 59, 60, 75
Cyclamen, 68
Cyclosis, 20
Cytomembrane, 22–3
Cytoplasm, 15, 24–6

Danielli membrane, 23
Dark CO_2 fixation, 73, 131
Dendrograph, 94
Deplasmolysis, 30
Dialysis, 9
Differential permeability, 9–14, 24, 25
Diffuse porous wood, 48, 54
Diffusion, 6–14
Diffusion pressure, 7
Diffusion pressure deficit, 11–13, 27–33, 37–9, 90–4, 109, 111, 114–16
Diffusion shell, 65–8
Diffusion through stomata, 64–8
Diurnal periodicity, 70, 71, 73, 94, 98, 99
Drainage, 123

Electro-osmosis, 36
Elodea, 20, 136, 140, 141
Emulsion, 5, 21
Endodermis, 44–6
Endoplasmic reticulum, 22
Ephedra, 134
Eucalyptus, 91
Euphorbia, 124
Euphorbiaceae, 124
Exodermis, 44

Fats, 21
Fibro-tracheid, 55
Field capacity, 109–14
Fuchsia, 57, 58, 59, 63, 99

Gel, 5, 20
Glyceria, 136
Golgi body, 22
Growth rings, 48
Guard cell, 63, 68–74
Guard cell of xerophyte, 125, 126, 127, 128
Guttation, 101, 102–3

Hakea, 125, 126, 127, 129, 134
Halophyte, 134–5
Heartwood, 50
Heterophylly, 139
Hydathode, 103
Hydrangea, 70
Hydrogen bonding, 1–3, 18, 21
Hydrologic cycle, 105–6
Hydrophyte, 123, 135–41
Hypertonic, 14
Hypotonic, 14

Ilex, 125, 127
Imbibition, 6, 18, 20, 34, 42, 64, 88, 90, 99, 101, 111
Incipient plasmolysis, 30
Internal atmosphere, 17, 57, 137
Irrigation, 116–22
Isotonic, 14

Juncus, 135

Kleinia, 124

Lactuca, 129
Lacuna, 137
Leaf anatomy of mesophyte, 56–60
Leaf anatomy of xerophyte, 124–9
Leaf epidermis, 57–9
Leaf lamina, 56
Lemna, 136, 139
Lenticel, 61–2
Leucoplast, 17
Lignification, 17, 40, 42, 45, 50–56, 106, 132–4

Lipids, 21
Lloyd, 76
Lycopus, 136
Lysimeter, 85
Lythrum, 136

Macrofibril, 18
Mentha, 135
Meristem, 42, 43
Mesophyll, 57, 90
Mesophyte, 123
Metaxylem, 42, 49, 55
Micelle, 19
Mıcrofibril, 18
Midday closure of stomata, 75
Middle lamella, 17
Midrib, 57
Mitochondrion, 15, 23, 24
Molisch's infiltration method, 77
Mulching, 122
Myriophyllum, 137
Myosotis, 135

Nerium, 125, 127
Nitella, 33
Nuclear membrane, 15
Nucleolus, 15
Nucleus, 15
Nuphar, 141
Nymphaea, 136, 138, 139

Opuntia, 124
Osmosis, 9–14, 26–34, 90
Osmotic potential, 13–14, 24, 27–34, 93–4, 115–16
Osmotic pressure, 12–13
Oxalis, 129

Papilionaceae, 134
Parallel venation, 57
Parenchymatous cell, 15–23, 39
Passage cell, 46
Pelargonium, 63, 64
Perforation, 53, 54, 55
Permanent wilting percentage, 112–15, 117, 118
Petiole, 57, 133
Pfeffer, 13
Phloem, 46, 49, 58

Phospholipid, 21, 22
Phragmites, 136
Phyllode, 133
Piliferous layer, 42
Pinus, 127, 129
Pit chamber, 52
Pit membrane, 52–3, 55
Pit pair, 17, 52, 56
Pitted element, 55
Plantago, 134
Plasmalemma, 15, 22, 24, 25
Plasmodesmata, 17, 25, 50, 90
Plasmolysis, 28–34
Plasmolyticum, 29
Plasmometric method, 33
Plastid, 17
Poa, 127
Porometer, 78–80
Potamogeton, 138, 139, 140
Potential transpiration, 118–19
Potometer, 85–7
Primary wall, 17, 18, 19
Protophloem, 42
Protoplasm, 19–23
Protoxylem, 42, 49, 54
Pubescence, 127–8

Ranunculus, 136, 139
Relative humidity, 81, 82, 92
Reticulate venation, 57
Ribosome, 22
Ring porous wood, 48, 54
Robinia, 129
Root anatomy, 41–6
Root cap, 41–2
Root constant, 119
Root hair, 42–3, 91
Root pressure, 99–100, 102–3
Ruscus, 132, 133

Sagittaria, 136, 139, 140
Salicornia, 134
Salt uptake, 19, 26, 88, 100
Sapwood, 50
Sclerenchyma, 40, 132–4
Scrophularia, 135
Secondary wall, 17, 19
Sequoia, 91, 94
Shade leaf, 58, 107

Simple pit, 17, 50, 53–4
Soil moisture, 109–23
Sol, 5, 20
Sparganium, 136
Specific heat, 2
Sphagnum, 135
Spines, 133–4
Spiral element, 54, 55
Spirogyra, 31
Stahl's cobalt chloride method, 77
Sterol, 21
Stoma, 58–60, 61–84, 92, 102
Stoma of xerophyte, 125–8, 131
Suberization, 17, 26, 44, 45
Subsidiary cell, 64, 68–70
Succulence, 70, 73, 129–31, 134–5
Sun leaf, 58, 107
Switch plant, 134

Thixotropy, 5, 20
Tilia, 47, 48
Tonoplast, 15, 22, 24
Torus, 52–54
Tracheid, 50–4, 55, 95, 96
Tradescantia, 33, 68
Transpiration, 61–99
Transpiration checks, 124–9
Turgor, 28–31, 39–40, 68, 70–1
Tugor pressure, 27–31
Turion, 139–40
Tylose, 50
Tyndall effect, 4
Typha, 136

Ulex, 133
Unavailable water, 113
Utricularia, 136, 140

Vaccinium, 135
Vacuole, 15, 24
Vallisneria, 140
Vapour pressure, 8, 81, 82, 84
Vascular ray, 49–50
Vein islet, 57
Vessel, 48, 50, 54–5
Viscosity, 3, 20

Wall pressure, 27–30, 109
Water deficit, 73–4, 98–9, 107, 108

Water erosion, 105, 106
Water pollination, 140–1
Water table, 105, 110
Water uptake by cells, 26–31, 34–9
Water uptake by roots, 97–102, 110–16
Wilting, 40, 74, 75, 76, 107–109, 111–115, 132
Wilting coefficient, 112
Winter bud, 139–40

Xeromorphic, 134–5
Xerophyte, 123, 124–35
Xeroplastic, 106
Xylem, 41–2, 44, 46–56, 58, 90
Xylem fibre, 50, 55–6
Xylem parenchyma, 50, 56, 101–2
Xylem tension, 53, 94–7

Zostera, 141